RELIGIOUS FAVORITES

Arranged for Piano by James Bastien

The Bastien Older Beginner Piano Library

PREFACE

RELIGIOUS FAVORITES is designed as a practical, in-depth reference anthology and contains a wide variety of well-known religious music arranged for easy piano. This volume may be chosen to supplement **THE OLDER BEGINNER PIANO COURSE** and may be assigned a **LEVEL 1** and continued into **LEVEL 2**. In addition this volume may be used as supplementary enrichment with any other piano course or as an independent book.

This collection may be used for sight reading, accompaniment, and in various church activities. Stanzas of the lyrics are included to provide a complete, useful reference source. The timeless appeal of these well-known religious favorites will provide hours of enjoyment for the pianist and listener.

Suggested Use of Materials with THE OLDER BEGINNER PIANO COURSE, LEVEL 1

When the student reaches **page 5**, he is ready to begin	**Musicianship, Level 1** (WP34)
When the student reaches **page 14**, he is ready to begin	**Music Flashcards** (GP27)
When the student reaches **page 15**, he is ready to begin	**Notespeller, Level 1** (WP20)
When the student reaches **page 44**, he is ready to begin	**Classic Themes by the Masters** (WP40)
When the student reaches **page 46**, he is ready to begin	**Religious Favorites** (WP41)
When the student reaches **page 48**, he is ready to begin	**Favorite Melodies the World Over, Level 1** (WP37)
When the student reaches **page 53**, he is ready to begin	**Pop, Rock 'N Blues, Book 1** (GP37)

Published by Kjos West.
National Order Desk, 4382 Jutland Dr., San Diego, CA 92117

ISBN 0-8497-5041-5

Topical Index

TRADITIONAL HYMNS
(including Catholic and Communion Hymns) 9
Abide with Me 19
All Glory, Laud and Honor 56
All Hail the Power of Jesus' Name 30
A Mighty Fortress is Our God 60
Beneath the Cross of Jesus 54
Blest Be the Tie That Binds 31
Break Thou the Bread of Life 46
Come, Christians, Join to Sing 50
Come Holy Ghost 36
Come, Thou Almighty King 10
Crown Him with Many Crowns 57
Fairest Lord Jesus.............................. 35
Faith of Our Fathers 14
For the Beauty of the Earth 16
Glorious Things of Thee Are Spoken 48
Glory Be to the Father........................... 51
God of Our Fathers 58
Glod, That Madest Earth and Heaven.............. 52
Holy God, We Praise Thy Name 37
Holy, Holy, Holy 53
I Love Thy Kingdom, Lord 42
In the Cross of Christ I Glory 45
I Would Be True 39
Jesus Calls Us 33
Jesus, Lover of My Soul 24
Jesus Shall Reign 13
Jesus, The Very Thought of Thee 40
Joyful, Joyful, We Adore Thee 41
Lead On, O King Eternal 26
Let Us With a Gladsome Mind 49
Love Divine, All Loves Excelling 59
More Love to Thee.............................. 20
My Faith Looks Up to Thee 11
My God, How Endless is Thy Love 47
Nearer, My God, to Thee........................ 38
O Master, Let Me Walk with Thee 23
Onward Christian Soldiers 28
O Worship the King 43
Praise God from Whom all Blessings Flow.......... 17
Praise to the Lord.............................. 22
Rock of Ages 34
Stand Up, Stand Up for Jesus 27
Sun of My Soul 18
Take My Life, and Let It Be 44
The Church's One Foundation 32
The King of Love My Shepherd Is 55
We Gather Together 21
When I Survey the Wondrous Corss 12
GOSPEL, SPIRITUAL, AND FOLK HYMNS 61
Amazing Grace................................. 64
Amen 98
Battle Hymn of the Republic 70
Beautiful Isle of Somewhere 78
Beulah Land 72
Bringing in the Sheaves 69
Give Me That Old Time Religion 88
Go Tell It on the Mountain 90
He Leadeth Me................................. 66
He's Got the Whole World in His Hands 96
In the Sweet By and By 86

I've Found a Friend 77
Jacob's Ladder 97
Jesus, Keep Me Near the Cross.................... 76
Jesus Saves 74
Joy, Joy, Joy 84
Just a Closer Walk with Thee..................... 62
Just as I Am 68
Kum-Ba-Ya 100
Let Us Break Bread Together 99
Nobody Knows the Trouble I've Seen 89
Shall We Gather At the River?.................... 67
Softly and Tenderly Jesus is Calling................ 82
Steal Away 93
Swing Low, Sweet Chariot 92
Sweet Hour of Prayer 80
Were You There? 87
What a Friend We Have in Jesus 65
When the Saints Go Marching In 94
Work, for the Night Is Coming 75
HYMNS FOR SPECIAL OCCASIONS
(including Thanksgiving, Christmas, Easter, and
Weddings 101
Thanksgiving
Come, Ye Thankful People, Come 102
Now Thank We All Our God 103
Sing To the Lord of Harvest 106
We Plow the Fields and Scatter................... 104
Christmas
Angels We Have Heard on High 113
Away in a Manger 107
Hark! The Herald Angels Sing 112
Joy to the World 108
O Come All Ye Faithful.......................... 117
O Little Town of Bethlehem...................... 116
Silent Night................................... 114
The First Noel 110
Easter
Come, Ye Faithful, Raise the Strain 119
Jesus Christ is Risen Today 118
The Day of Resurrection 121
The Strife is O'er 120
Wedding
O Perfect Love 122
HYMNS FOR CHILDREN 123
All Things Bright and Beautiful 124
Faith 137
Father, Lead Me Day by Day..................... 134
Father, We Thank Thee for the Night 130
God's Touch 138
God's Watch 136
Jesus Loves Me 126
Jesus Loves the Little Children 132
Jesus Wants Me for a Sunbeam 127
Little Drops of Water 128
Praise Him, All Ye Little Children 133
Sunday Morning 135
Tell Me the Stories of Jesus 131
This is My Father's World 129
CONTEMPORARY HYMNS 139
Count Your Blessings 142
Lord, You Are My Sunshine 140

4

Contents

-A-
Abide with Me 19
All Glory, Laud and Honor 56
All Hail the Power of Jesus' Name 30
All Things Bright and Beautiful 124
Amazing Grace 64
Amen 98
A Mighty Fortress is Our God 60
Angels We Have Heard on High 113
Away in a Manger 107

-B-
Battle Hymn of the Republic 70
Beautiful Isle of Somewhere 78
Beneath the Cross of Jesus 54
Beulah Land 72
Blest Be the Tie That Binds 31
Break Thou the Bread of Life 46
Bringing in the Sheaves 69

-C-
Come, Christians, Join to Sing 50
Come, Holy Ghost 36
Come, Thou Almighty King 10
Come, Ye Faithful, Raise the Strain 119
Come, Ye Thankful People, Come 102
Count Your Blessings 142
Crown Him with Many Crowns 57

-F-
Fairest Lord Jesus 35
Faith 137
Faith of Our Fathers 14
Father, Lead Me Day by Day 134
Father, We Thank Thee for the Night 130
For the Beauty of the Earth 16

-G-
Give Me That Old Time Religion 88
Glorious Things of Thee Are Spoken 48
Glory Be to the Father 51
God of Our Fathers 58
God's Touch 138
God's Watch 136
God, That Madest Earth and Heaven 52
Go Tell It on the Mountain 90

-H-
Hark! The Herald Angels Sing 112
He Leadeth Me 66
He's Got the Whole World in His Hands 96
Holy God, We Praise Thy Name 37
Holy, Holy, Holy 53

-I-
I Love Thy Kingdom, Lord 42
In the Cross of Christ I Glory 45
In the Sweet By and By 86
I've Found a Friend 77
I Would Be True 39

-J-
Jacob's Ladder 97
Jesus Calls Us 33
Jesus Christ is Risen Today 118
Jesus, Keep Me Near the Cross 76
Jesus, Lover of My Soul 24
Jesus Loves Me 126
Jesus Loves the Little Children 132
Jesus Saves 74
Jesus Shall Reign 13
Jesus, The Very Thought of Thee 40
Jesus Wants Me for a Sunbeam 127

Joyful, Joyful, We Adore Thee 41
Joy, Joy, Joy 84
Joy to the World 108
Just a Closer Walk with Thee 62
Just As I Am 68
-K-
Kum-Ba-Ya 100
-L-
Lead On, O King Eternal 26
Let Us Break Bread Together 99
Let Us With a Gladsome Mind 49
Little Drops of Water 128
Lord, You Are My Sunshine 140
Love Divine, All Loves Excelling 59
-M-
More Love to Thee 20
My Faith Looks Up to Thee 11
My God, How Endless Is Thy Love 47
-N-
Nearer, My God, to Thee 38
Nobody Knows the Trouble I've Seen 89
Now Thank We All Our God 103
-O-
O Come, All Ye Faithful 117
O Perfect Love 122
O Little Town of Bethlehem 116
O Master, Let Me Walk with Thee 23
Onward, Christian Soldiers 28
O Worship the King 43
-P-
Praise God from Whom All Blessings Flow 17
Praise Him, All Ye Little Children 133
Praise to the Lord 22
-R-
Rock of Ages 34
-S-
Shall We Gather At the River? 67
Silent Night 114
Sing To the Lord of Harvest 106
Softly and Tenderly Jesus is Calling 82
Stand Up, Stand Up for Jesus 27
Steal Away 93
Sunday Morning 135
Sun of My Soul 18
Sweet Hour of Prayer 80
Swing Low, Sweet Chariot 92
-T-
Take My Life, and Let It Be 44
Tell Me the Stories of Jesus 131
The Church's One Foundation 32
The Day of Resurrection 121
The First Noel 110
The King of Love My Shepherd Is 55
The Strife is O'er 120
This is My Father's World 129
-W-
We Gather Together 21
We Plow the Fields and Scatter 104
Were You There? 87
What a Friend We Have in Jesus 65
When I Survey the Wondrous Cross 12
When the Saints Go Marching In 94
Work, for the Night Is Coming 75

CHORD PRACTICE

The harmony used mostly in this book consists of I, IV, V7 chords in the keys of C, G, F, D Major and some minor chords. Therefore, these are given here for study and reference. These chords may be practiced separately for preparation in playing the hymn arrangements.

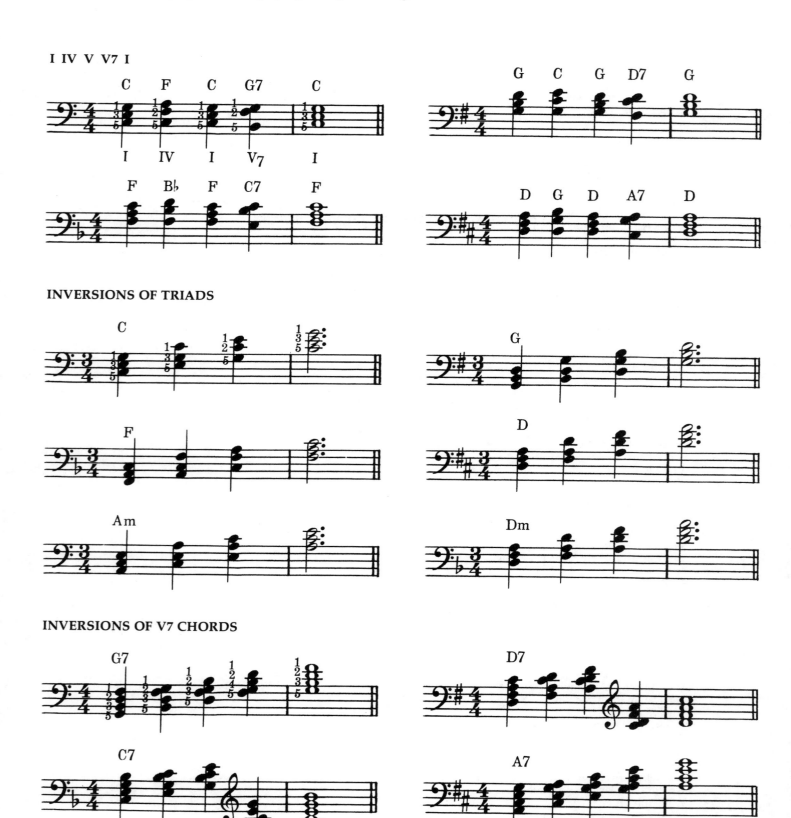

Religious Favorites

Arranged for Piano by James Bastien

TRADITIONAL HYMNS

(including Catholic and Communion Hymns)

10

Come, Thou Almighty King

Felice de Giardini
(1716-1796)

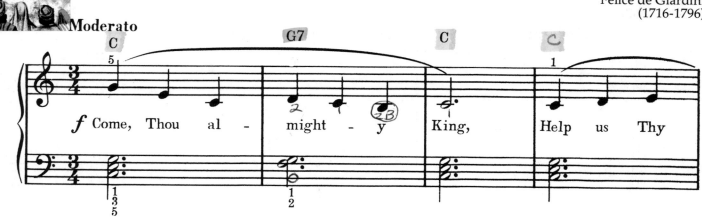

Moderato

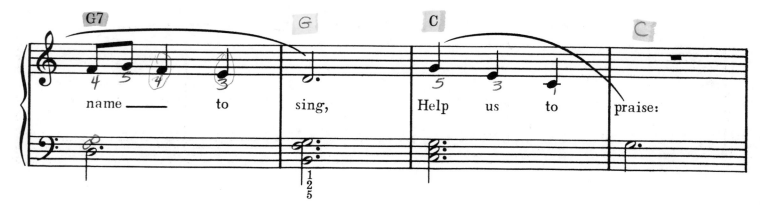

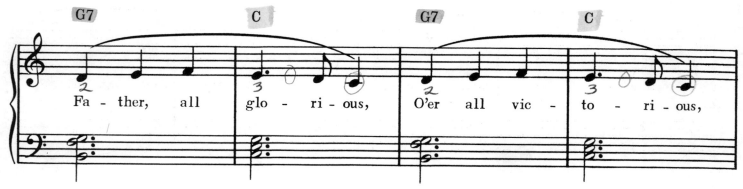

2. Come, Thou Incarnate Word,
Gird on Thy mighty sword,
Our prayer attend:
Come, and Thy people bless,
And give Thy Word success;
Spirit of holiness,
On us descend.

3. Come, Holy Comforter,
Thy sacred witness bear
In this glad hour:
Thou Who almighty art,
Now rule in every heart,
And ne'er from us depart,
Spirit of power.

4. To Thee, great One in Three,
Eternal praises be
Hence, evermore.
His sovereign majesty
May we in glory see,
And to eternity
Love and adore.

(WP41)

My Faith Looks Up to Thee

Ray Palmer
(1808-1887)

Lowell Mason
(1792-1872)

2. May Thy rich grace impart
Strength to my fainting heart,
My zeal inspire;
As Thou hast died for me,
O may my love to Thee
Pure, warm, and changeless be,
A living fire!

3. While life's dark maze I tread,
And griefs around me spread,
Be Thou my Guide:
Bid darkness turn to day,
Wipe sorrow's tears away,
Nor let me ever stray
From Thee aside.

4. When ends life's transient dream,
When death's cold sullen stream
Shall o'er me roll,
Blest Savior, then, in love,
Fear and distrust remove;
O bear me safe above,
A ransomed soul!

When I Survey the Wondrous Cross

Gregorian Chant
Adapted by Lowell Mason
(1792-1872)

2. Forbid it, Lord, that I should boast,
   Save in the death of Christ my God:
   All the vain things that charm me most,
   I sacrifice them to His blood.

3. See, from His head, His hands, His feet,
   Sorrow and love flow mingled down:
   Did e'er such love and sorrow meet,
   Or thorns compose so rich a crown?

4. Were the whole realm of nature mine,
   That were a present far too small;
   Love so amazing, so divine,
   Demands my soul, my life, my all.

Jesus Shall Reign

Isaac Watts
(1674-1748)

John Hatton
(1710-1793)

With spirit

Je - sus shall reign wher - e're the ___ sun

Does his suc - ces - sive jour - neys run,

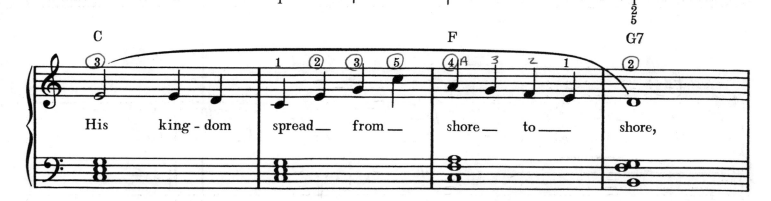

His king - dom spread ___ from ___ shore ___ to ___ shore,

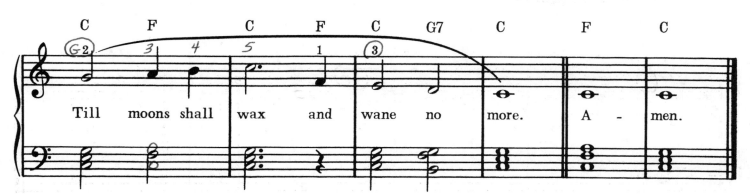

Till moons shall wax and wane no more. A - men.

2. For Him shall endless prayer be made,
   And praises throng to crown His head;
   His name, like sweet perfume, shall rise
   With every morning sacrifice.

3. People and realms of every tongue
   Dwell on His love with sweetest song,
   And infant voices shall proclaim
   Their early blessings on His name.

4. Blessings abound where'er He reigns;
   The prisoner leaps to loose his chains,
   The weary find eternal rest,
   And all the sons of want are blest.

5. Let every creature rise and bring
   Peculiar honors to our King;
   Angels descend with songs again,
   And earth repeat the loud amen!

(WP41)

Faith of Our Fathers

Frederick W. Faber
(1814-1863)

Henri F. Hemy
(1818-1888)
Adapted by James G. Walton
(1821-1905)

Faith of our fa - thers, liv - ing still

In spite of dun - geon, fire___ and sword,

O how our hearts___ beat high___ with joy

When - e'er we hear that glo - rious word!

(WP41)

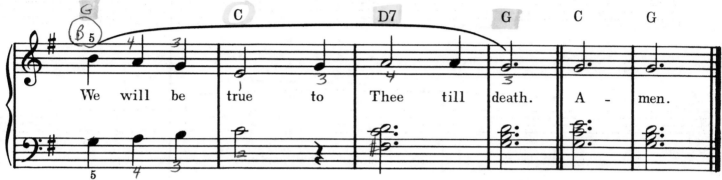

2. Our fathers, chained in prisons dark,
   Were still in heart and conscience free,
   And blest would be their children's fate,
   If they, like them should die for thee.
   Refrain:

3. Faith of our fathers, faith and prayer
   Shall keep our country brave and free,
   And through the truth that comes from
     God,
   Our land shall then indeed be free.
   Refrain:

4. Faith of our fathers, we will love
   Both friend and foe in all our strife,
   And preach thee, too, as love knows how
   By kindly words and virtuous life:
   Refrain:

For the Beauty of the Earth

Folliott S. Pierpoint
(1835-1917)

Adapted from a chorale by
Conrad Kocher
(1786-1872)

2. For the wonder of each hour
Of the day and of the night,
Hill and vale and tree and flower,
Sun and moon, and stars of light:
Refrain:

3. For the joy of human love,
Brother, sister, parent, child,
Friends on earth, and friends above;
For all gentle thoughts and mild:
Refrain:

4. For Thy Church that evermore
Lifteth holy hands above,
Offering up on every shore
Her pure sacrifice of love:
Refrain:

Praise God from Whom All Blessings Flow

(Doxology)

Thomas Ken
(1637-1711)

from the "Genevan Psalter"
Attributed to Louis Bourgeois
(1510-1561)

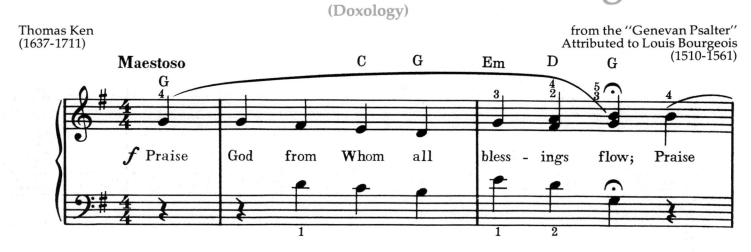

f Praise God from Whom all bless - ings flow; Praise

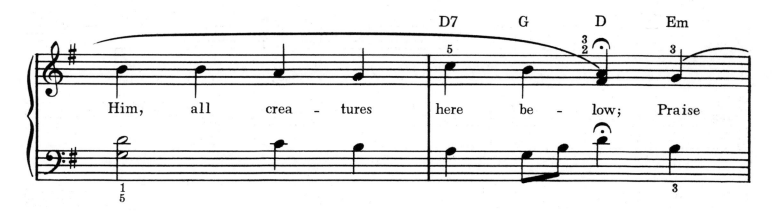

Him, all crea - tures here be - low; Praise

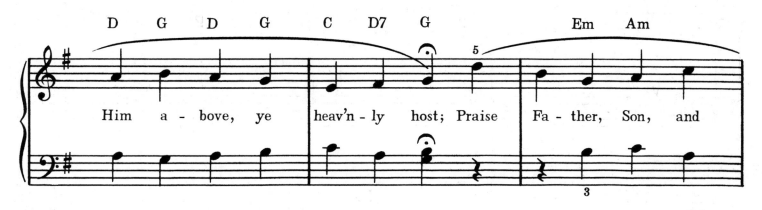

Him a - bove, ye heav'n - ly host; Praise Fa - ther, Son, and

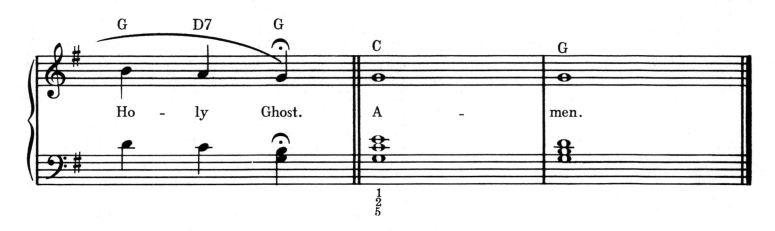

Ho - ly Ghost. A - men.

(WP41)

Sun of My Soul

John Keble
(1792-1866)

from "Katholisches Gesangbuch" (1774)
Peter Ritter

Moderato

mf Sun of my soul, ___ Thou Sav - iour dear,

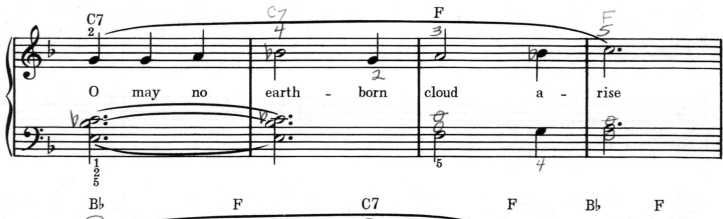

It is not night ___ if Thou ___ be near;

O may no earth - born cloud a - rise

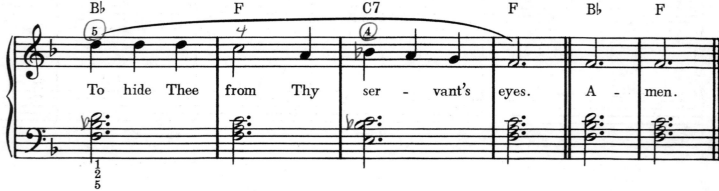

To hide Thee from Thy ser - vant's eyes. A - men.

2. When the soft dews of kindly sleep
   My wearied eyelids gently steep,
   Be my last thought how sweet to rest
   Forever on my Saviour's breast.

3. Abide with me from morn till eve,
   For without Thee I cannot live;
   Abide with me when night is nigh,
   For without Thee I dare not die.

4. Watch by the sick, enrich the poor
   With blessings from Thy boundless store;
   Be every mourner's sleep tonight,
   Like infants; slumbers, pure and light.

5. Come near and bless us when we wake,
   Ere through the world our way we take,
   Till in the ocean of Thy love
   We lose ourselves in heav'n above.

(WP41)

Abide With Me

Henry F. Lyte
(1793-1847)

William H. Monk
(1823-1889)

2. Swift to its close ebbs out life's little day;
Earth's joys grow dim, its glories pass
away;
Change and decay in all around I see;
O Thou Who changes not, abide with me.

3. I need Thy presence every passing hour;
What but Thy grace can foil the tempter's
power?
Who, like Thyself, my guide and stay can
be?
Through cloud and sunshine, Lord, abide
with me.

4. I fear no foe, with Thee at hand to bless;
Ills have no weight, and tears no
bitterness:
Where is death's sting? Where, grave, thy
victory?
I triumph still, if Thou abide with me.

5. Hold Thou Thy cross before my closing
eyes;
Shine through the gloom, and point me
to the skies:
Heav'n's morning breaks, and earth's
vain shadows flee;
In life, in death, O Lord, abide with me.

(WP41)

More Love to Thee

Love One Another

Elizabeth P. Prentiss
(1818-1878)

W. H. Doane
(1832-1915)

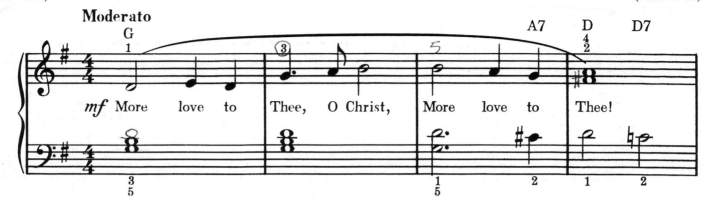

More love to Thee, O Christ, More love to Thee!

Hear Thou the prayer I make On bend-ed knee;

This is my ear-nest plea, More love, O Christ, to Thee,

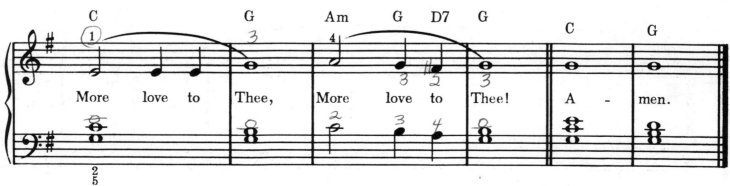

More love to Thee, More love to Thee! A - men.

2. Once earthly joy I craved,
   Sought peace and rest;
   Now Thee alone I seek;
   Give what is best;
   This all my prayer shall be,
   More love, O Christ, to Thee,
   More love to Thee,
   More love to Thee!

3. Then shall my latest breath
   Whisper Thy praise;
   This be the parting cry
   My heart shall raise;
   This still its prayer shall be,
   More love, O Christ, to Thee,
   More love to Thee,
   More love to Thee!

(WP41)

We Gather Together

Netherlands Folk Song
Translated by Theodore Baker
(1851-1934)

Netherlands Tune
Adapted by Edward Kremer
(1838-1914)

2. Beside us to guide us, our God with us joining,
   Ordaining, maintaining His kingdom divine,
   So from the beginning the fight we were winning;
   Thou, Lord, wast at our side, all glory be Thine.

3. We all do extol Thee, Thou Leader triumphant,
   And pray that Thou still our defender wilt be.
   Let Thy congregation escape tribulation!
   Thy name be ever praised! O Lord, make us free!

Praise to the Lord

Joachim Neander
(1650-1680)
Translated by Catherine Winkworth
(1829-1878)

from "...book" (1665)

Praise to the Lord, the Al - might-y, the King of cre - a - tion!

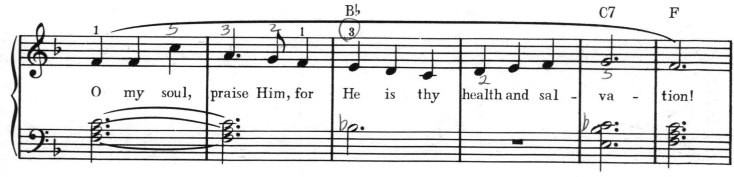

O my soul, praise Him, for He is thy health and sal - va - tion!

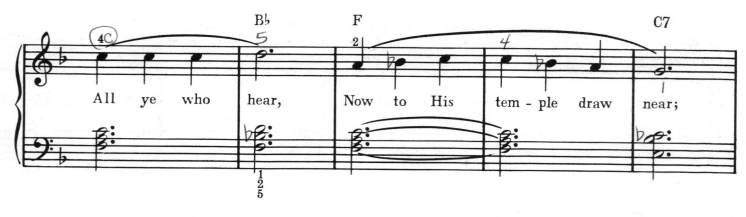

All ye who hear, Now to His tem - ple draw near;

Join me in glad ad - o - ra - tion! A - men.

2. Praise to the Lord, who o'er all things so
    wondrously reigneth,
   Shelters thee under His wings, yea, so
    gently sustaineth!
   Hast thou not seen how thy desires e'er
    have been
   Granted in what He ordaineth?

3. Praise to the Lord! O let all that is in me
    adore Him!
   All that hath life and breath, come now
    with praises before Him!
   Let the amen sound from His people
    again:
   Gladly for aye we adore Him.

O Master, Let Me Walk With Thee

Washington Gladden
(1836-1918)

Henry Percy Smith
(1825-1898)

O Mas-ter, let me walk with Thee

In low-ly paths of serv - ice free;

Tell me Thy se - cret; help ___ me bear The

strain of toil, the fret of care. A - men.

2. Help me the slow of heart to move
By some clear, winning word of love;
Teach me the wayward feet to stay,
And guide them in the homeward way.

3. Teach me Thy patience; still with Thee
In closer, dearer company,
In work that keeps faith sweet and
strong,
In trust that triumphs over wrong.

4. In hope that sends a shining ray
Far down the future's broadening way;
In peace that only Thou canst give,
With Thee, O Master, let me live.

Jesus, Lover of My Soul

Charles Wesley
(1707-1788)

Simeon B. Marsh
(1798-1875)

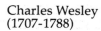

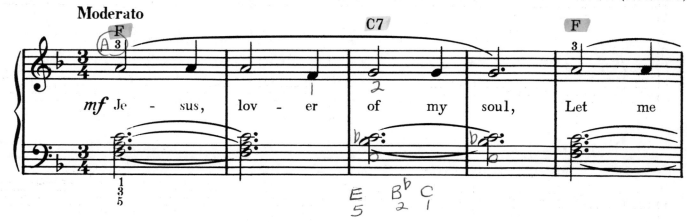

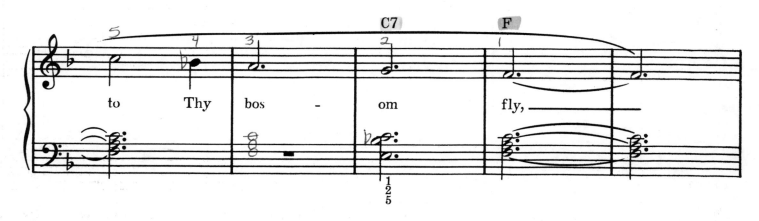

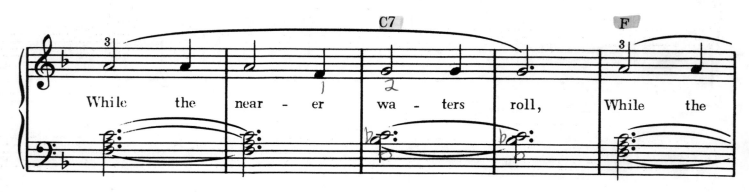

2. Other refuge have I none,
   Hangs my helpless soul on Thee:
   Leave, ah, leave me not alone,
   Still support and comfort me.
   All my trust on Thee is stayed,
   All my help from Thee I bring;
   Cover my defenseless head
   With the shadow of Thy wing.

3. Plenteous grace with Thee is found,
   Grace to cleanse from all my sin;
   Let the healing streams abound,
   Make and keep me pure within.
   Thou of life the fountain art;
   Freely let me take of Thee;
   Spring Thou up within my heart,
   Rise to all eternity.

Lead On, O King Eternal

Ernest W. Shurtleff
(1862-1917)

Henry Smart
(1813-1879)

2. Lead on, O King Eternal,
Till sin's fierce war shall cease,
And holiness shall whisper
The sweet amen of peace;
For not with swords, loud clashing,
Nor roll of stirring drums,
With deeds of love and mercy,
The heavenly kingdom comes.

3. Lead on, O King Eternal,
We follow, not with fears,
For gladness breaks like morning
Where'er Thy face appears:
Thy cross is lifted o'er us;
We journey in its light;
The crown awaits the conquest;
Lead on, O God of might.

(WP41)

Stand Up, Stand Up for Jesus

George Duffield
(1818-1888)

George J. Webb
(1803-1887)

With spirit

Stand up, stand up for Jesus Ye sol-diers of the cross; Lift high His roy-al ban-ner, It must not suf-fer loss. From vic-tory un-to vic-tory, His ar-my He shall lead,____ Till ev-ery foe is van-quished, And Christ is Lord in-deed! A-men.

2. Stand up, stand up for Jesus,
   The trumpet call obey;
   Forth to the mighty conflict,
   In this His glorious day:
   Ye that are men now serve Him
   Against unnumbered foes;
   Let courage rise with danger,
   And strength to strength oppose.

3. Stand up, stand up for Jesus,
   Stand in His strength alone;
   The arm of flesh will fail you,
   Ye dare not trust your own:
   Put on the gospel armor,
   Each piece put on with prayer;
   Where duty calls, or danger,
   Be never wanting there.

4. Stand up, stand up for Jesus,
   The strife will not be long;
   This day the noise of battle,
   The next, the victor's song:
   To him that overcometh
   A crown of life shall be;
   He with the King of Glory
   Shall reign eternally.

Onward, Christian Soldiers

Sabine Baring-Gould
(1834-1924)

Arthur S. Sullivan
(1842-1900)

C Position

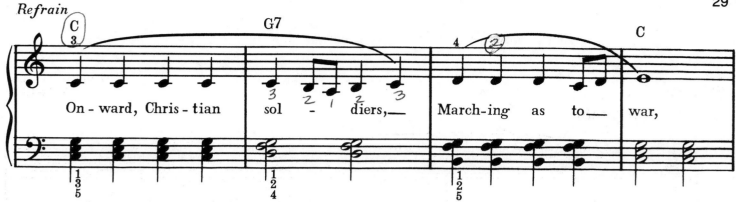

2. Like a mighty army
Moves the Church of God;
Brothers, we are treading
Where the saints have trod;
We are not divided,
All one body we,
One in hope and doctrine,
One in charity.
Refrain:

3. Crowns and thrones may perish,
Kingdoms rise and wane,
But the Church of Jesus
Constant will remain;
Gates of hell can never
'Gainst that Church prevail;
We have Christ's own promise,
And that cannot fail.
Refrain:

4. Onward, then, ye people,
Join our happy throng,
Blend with ours your voices
In the triumph song;
Glory, laud, and honor
Unto Christ the King;
This through countless ages
Men and angels sing.
Refrain:

All Hail the Power of Jesus' Name

Edward Perronet
(1726-1792)

Oliver Holden
(1765-1844)

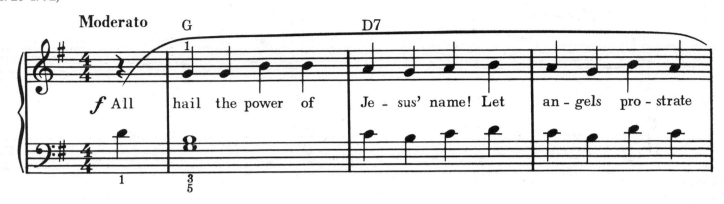

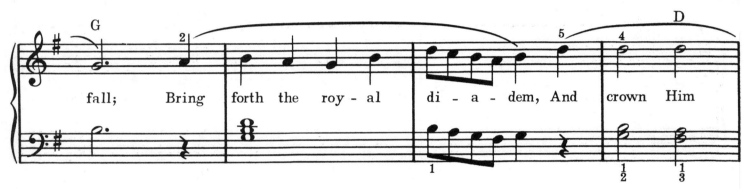

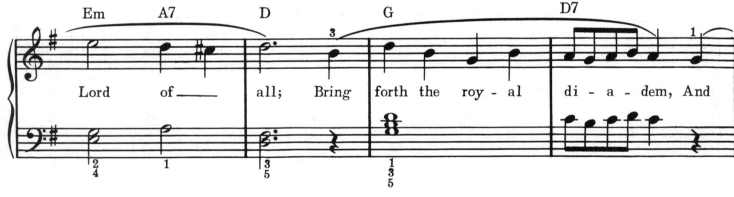

2. Let every kindred, every tribe,
   On this terrestrial ball,
   To Him all majesty ascribe,
   And crown Him Lord of all;
   To Him all majesty ascribe,
   And crown Him Lord of all!

3. O, that with yonder sacred throng
   We at His feet may fall,
   We'll join the everlasting song,
   And crown him Lord of all;
   We'll join the everlasting song,
   And crown Him Lord of all!

Blest Be the Tie That Binds

John Fawcett
(1789-1817)

Hans G. Nägeli
(1773-1836)

Blest be the tie that binds Our hearts in Chris - tian love; The fel - low - ship of kin - dred minds Is like to that a - bove. A - men.

2. Before our Father's throne
We pour our ardent prayers;
Our fears, our hopes, our aims are one,
Our comforts and our cares.

3. We share our mutual woes,
Our mutual burdens bear,
And often for each other flows
The sympathizing tear.

4. When we asunder part,
It gives us inward pain;
But we shall still be joined in heart,
And hope to meet again.

The Church's One Foundation

Samuel J. Stone
(1839-1900)

Samuel S. Wesley
(1810-1876)

The Church's one foun-da-tion Is Je-sus Christ her Lord; She is His new cre-a-tion By wa-ter and the word: From heaven He came and sought her To be His ho-ly bride; With His own blood He bought her, And for her life He died. A-men.

2. Elect from every nation,
   Yet one o'er all the earth,
   Her charter of salvation
   One Lord, one faith, one birth;
   One holy name she blesses,
   Partakes one holy food,
   And to one hope she presses,
   With every grace endued.

3. 'Mid toil and tribulation,
   And tumult of her war,
   She waits the consummation
   Of peace for evermore;
   Till with the vision glorious
   Her longing eyes are blest,
   And the great Church victorious
   Shall be the Church at rest.

4. Yet she on earth hath union
   With God, the Three in One,
   And mystic sweet communion
   With those whose rest is won:
   O happy ones and holy!
   Lord, give us grace that we,
   Like them, the meek and lowly,
   On high may dwell with Thee.

Jesus Calls Us

Cecil F. Alexander
(1818-1895)

William H. Jude
(1851-1922)

2. Jesus calls us from the worship
   Of the vain world's golden store,
   From each idol that would keep us,
   Saying, "Christian, love Me more."

3. In our joys and in our sorrows,
   Days of toil and hours of ease,
   Still He calls, in cares and pleasures,
   "Christian, love Me more than these."

4. Jesus calls us; by Thy mercies,
   Saviour, may we hear Thy call,
   Give our hearts to Thine obedience,
   Serve and love Thee best of all.

Rock of Ages

Augustus M. Toplady
(1740-1778)

Thomas Hastings
(1784-1872)

2. Could my zeal no respite know,
   Could my tears forever flow,
   All for sin could not atone,
   Thou must save, and Thou alone;
   Nothing in my hand I bring,
   Simply to Thy cross I cling.

3. While I draw this fleeting breath,
   When mine eyes shall close in death,
   When I soar to worlds unknown,
   And behold Thee on Thy throne,
   Rock of ages, cleft for me,
   Let me hide myself in Thee.

Fairest Lord Jesus
(Crusader's Hymn)

German, 17th Century

Silesian Folk Tune

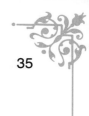

Fair - est Lord Je - sus, Rul - er of all na - ture,

O Thou of God and ___ man the Son,

Thee will I cher - ish, Thee will I hon - or, Thou,

my soul's glo - ry, joy, and crown. A - men.

2. Fair are the meadows,
   Fairer still the woodlands,
   Robed in the blooming garb of spring;
   Jesus is fairer,
   Jesus is purer,
   Who makes the woeful heart to sing.

3. Fair is the sunshine,
   Fairer still the moonlight,
   And all the twinkling, starry host;
   Jesus shines brighter,
   Jesus shines purer
   Than all the angels heaven can boast.

Come, Holy Ghost

(Hymn for Pentecost)

2. O Comforter, to Thee we cry,
   Thou heavenly Gift of God most high;
   Thou Fount of life and fire of love,
   And sweet annointing from above,
   And sweet annointing from above.

3. O Holy Ghost, through Thee alone
   Know we the Father and the Son,
   Be this our never changing creed,
   That Thou dost from them both proceed,
   That Thou dost from them both proceed.

4. Praise be the Father and the Son,
   And Holy Spirit with them one;
   And may the Son on us bestow
   The gifts that from the Spirit flow,
   The gifts that from the Spirit flow.

(WP41)

Holy God, We Praise Thy Name
(Hymn to the Holy Trinity)

"Te Deum," 4th Century
Translated by Clarence Walworth
(1820-1900)

From "Katholisches Gesangbuch" (1774)

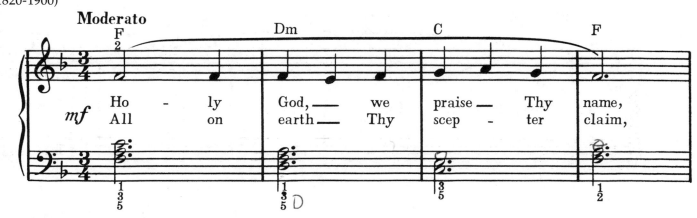

Holy God, we praise Thy name,
All on earth Thy scepter claim,

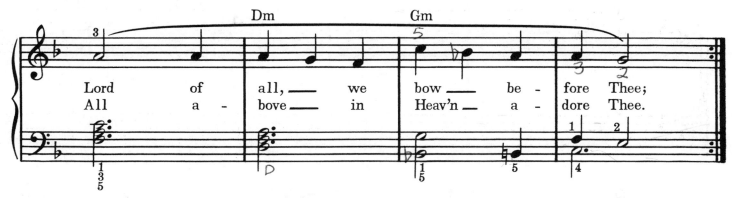

Lord of all, we bow before Thee;
All above in Heav'n adore Thee.

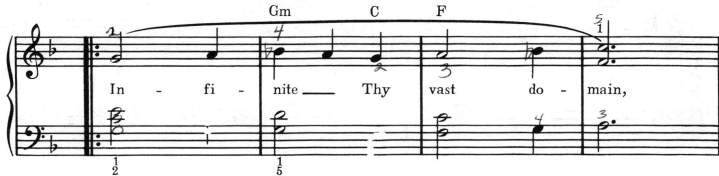

Infinite Thy vast domain,

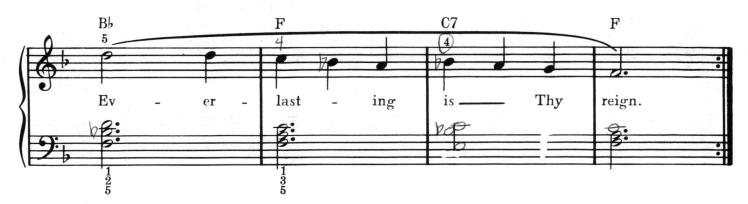

Everlasting is Thy reign.

2. Hark, the loud celestial hymn,
Angel choirs above are raising;
Cherubim and seraphim,
In unceasing chorus praising.
Fill the heav'ns with sweet accord;
Holy, holy, holy Lord.
Fill the heav'ns with sweet accord;
Holy, holy, holy Lord.

3. Holy Father, Holy Son,
Holy Spirit, Three we name Thee;
While in essence only One,
Undivided God we claim Thee.
And adoring, bend the knee,
While we own the mystery.
And adoring, bend the knee,
While we own the mystery.

Nearer, My God, to Thee

Sarah F. Adams
(1805-1848)

Lowell Mason
(1792-1872)

Moderato

Near-er, my God, to Thee, Near-er to Thee!

E'en though it be a cross That___ rais-eth me;

Still all my song shall be, Near-er, my God, to Thee,

Near-er, my God, to Thee, Near-er to Thee! A - men.

2. Though like the wanderer,
The sun gone down,
Darkness be over me,
My rest a stone,
Yet in my dreams I'd be,
Nearer, my God, to Thee,
Nearer, my God, to Thee,
Nearer to Thee!

3. There let the way appear,
Steps unto heaven;
All that Thou sendest me
In mercy given;
Angels to beckon me
Nearer, my God, to Thee,
Nearer, my God, to Thee,
Nearer to Thee!

4. Then, with my waking thoughts
Bright with Thy praise,
Out of my stony griefs
Bethel I'll raise;
So by my woes to be
Nearer, my God, to Thee,
Nearer, my God, to Thee,
Nearer to Thee!

5. Or if on joyful wing
Cleaving the sky,
Sun, moon, and stars forgot,
Upward I fly,
Still all my song shall be,
Nearer, my God, to Thee,
Nearer, my God, to Thee,
Nearer to Thee!

I Would Be True

Howard A. Walter
(1883-1918)

Joseph Yates Peek
(1834-1911)

(WP41)

Jesus, The Very Thought of Thee

Bernard of Clairvaux (1091-1153)
Translated by Edward Caswall (1814-1878)

John B. Dykes
(1823-1876)

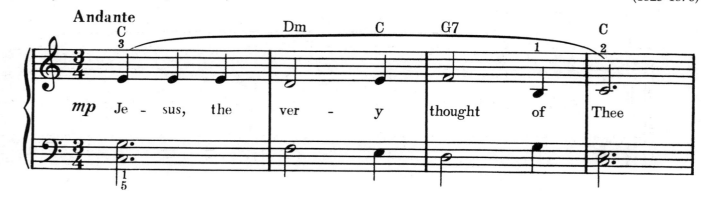

Jesus, the very thought of Thee

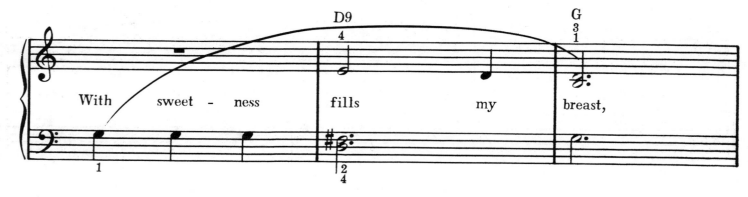

With sweetness fills my breast,

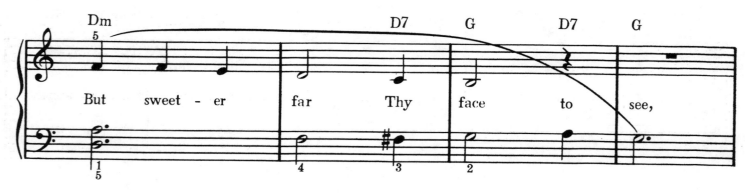

But sweeter far Thy face to see,

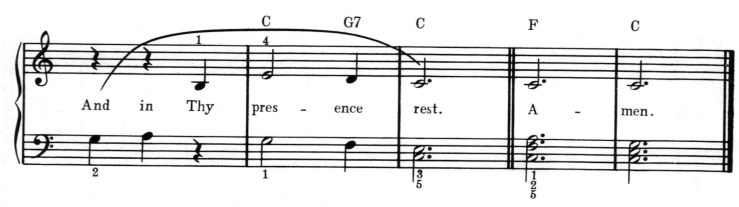

And in Thy presence rest. A - men.

2. Nor voice can sing, nor heart can frame,
Nor can the memory find
A sweeter sound than Thy blest name,
O Saviour of mankind!

3. O Hope of every contrite heart,
O Joy of all the meek,
To those who fall, how kind Thou art!
How good to those who seek!

4. But what to those who find? Ah, this
Nor tongue nor pen can show;
The love of Jesus, what it is,
None but His loved ones know.

5. Jesus, our only Joy be Thou,
As Thou our Prize wilt be;
Jesus, be Thou our Glory now,
And through eternity.

Joyful, Joyful, We Adore Thee

Henry Van Dyke
(1852-1933)

Ludwig Van Beethoven
(1770-1827)

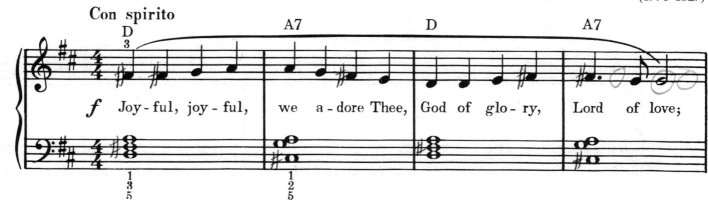

Joy-ful, joy-ful, we a-dore Thee, God of glo-ry, Lord of love;

Hearts un-fold like flowers be-fore Thee, Open-ing to the sun a-bove.

Melt the clouds of sin and sad-ness, Drive the dark of doubt a-way;

Giv-er of im-mor-tal glad-ness, Fill us with the light of day. A-men.

2. All Thy works in joy surround Thee,
Earth and heaven reflect Thy rays
Stars and angels sing around Thee,
Center of unbroken praise.
Field and forest, vale and mountain,
Flowery meadow, flashing sea,
Chanting bird and flowing fountain,
Call us to rejoice in Thee.

3. Thou art giving and forgiving,
Ever blessing, ever blest,
Well-spring of the joy of living,
Ocean depth of happy rest!
Thou our Father, Christ our Brother,
All who live in love are Thine;
Teach us how to love each other,
Lift us to the joy divine.

4. Mortals, join the happy chorus
Which the morning stars began;
Father love is reigning o'er us,
Brother love binds man to man.
Ever singing, march we onward,
Victors in the midst of strife,
Joyful music leads us sunward
In the triumph song of life.

(WP41)

I Love Thy Kingdom, Lord

Timothy Dwight
(1752-1817)

2. I love Thy church, O God:
   Her walls before Thee stand,
   Dear as the apple of Thine eye,
   And graven on Thy hand.

3. For her my tears shall fall,
   For her my prayers ascend;
   To her my cares and toils be given,
   Till toils and cares shall end.

4. Beyond my highest joy
   I prize her heavenly ways,
   Her sweet communion, solemn vows,
   Her hymns of love and praise.

5. Sure as Thy truth shall last,
   To Zion shall be given
   The brightest glories earth can yield,
   And brighter bliss of heaven.

O Worship the King

Sir Robert Grant
(1779-1838)

J. Michael Haydn
(1737-1806)

2. O tell of His might, O sing of His grace,
   Whose robe is the light, whose canopy
   space;
   His chariots of wrath the deep
   thunder-clouds form,
   And dark is His path on the wings of the
   storm.

3. Thy bountiful care what tongue can
   recite?
   It breathes in the air, it shines in the light;
   It streams from the hills, it descends to
   the plain,
   And sweetly distills in the dew and the
   rain.

4. Frail children of dust, and feeble as frail,
   In Thee do we trust, nor find Thee to fail;
   Thy mercies how tender, how firm to the
   end,
   Our Maker, Defender, Redeemer, and
   Friend.

Take My Life, and Let It Be

Frances R. Havergal
(1836-1879)

H. A. Cesar Malan
(1787-1864)

2. Take my hands, and let them move
At the impulse of Thy love.
Take my feet, and let them be
Swift and beautiful for Thee,
Swift and beautiful for Thee.

3. Take my voice, and let me sing,
Always, only, for my King.
Take my lips and let them be
Filled with messages from Thee,
Filled with messages from Thee.

4. Take my will, and make it Thine;
It shall be no longer mine.
Take my heart, it is Thine own;
It shall be Thy royal throne,
It shall be Thy royal throne.

5. Take my love; my Lord, I pour
At Thy feet its treasure store.
Take myself, and I will be
Ever, only, all for Thee,
Ever, only, all for Thee.

In the Cross of Christ I Glory

John Bowring
(1792-1872)

Ithamar Conkey
(1815-1867)

In the cross of Christ I glory,
Tow-'ring o'er the wrecks of time;
All the light of sa-cred sto-ry
Gath-ers round its head sub-lime. A-men.

2. When the woes of life o'ertake me,
   Hopes deceive, and fears annoy,
   Never shall the cross forsake me;
   Lo! it glows with peace and joy.

3. When the sun of bliss is beaming
   Light and love upon my way,
   From the cross the radiance streaming
   Adds new luster to the day.

4. Bane and blessing, pain and pleasure,
   By the cross are sanctified;
   Peace is there that knows no measure,
   Joys that through all time abide.

(WP41)

Break Thou the Bread of Life

Mary A. Lathbury
(1841-1913)

William F. Sherwin
(1826-1888)

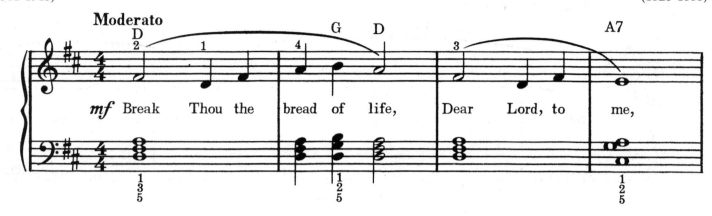

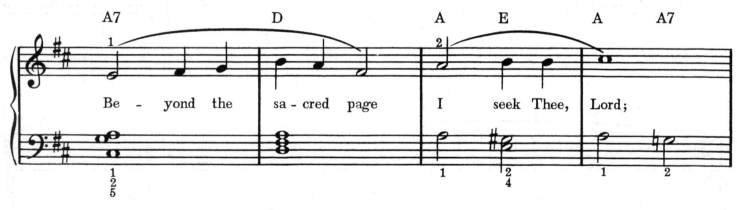

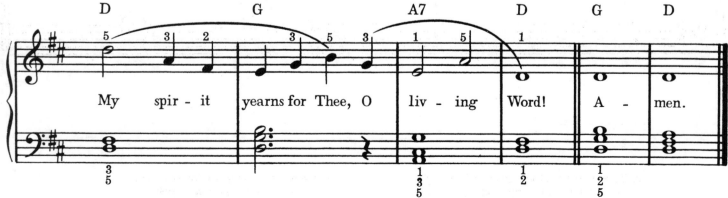

Lyrics in the music:

Break Thou the bread of life, Dear Lord, to me,
As Thou didst break the loaves Be - side the sea;
Be - yond the sa - cred page I seek Thee, Lord;
My spir - it yearns for Thee, O liv - ing Word! A - men.

2. Bless Thou the truth, dear Lord,
To me, to me,
As Thou didst bless the bread
By Galilee;
Then shall all bondage cease,
All fetters fall,
And I shall find my peace,
My all in all.

3. Thou art the bread of life,
Dear Lord, to me,
Thy holy word the truth
That saveth me;
Give me to eat and live
With Thee above;
Teach me to love Thy truth,
For Thou art love.

4. O send Thy Spirit, Lord
Now unto me,
That He may touch mine eyes,
And make me see;
Show me the truth concealed
Within Thy Word,
And in Thy Book revealed,
I see the Lord.

(WP41)

47

My God, How Endless Is Thy Love

Isaac Watts
(1674-1748)

Robert Schumann
(1810-1856)

Andante con moto

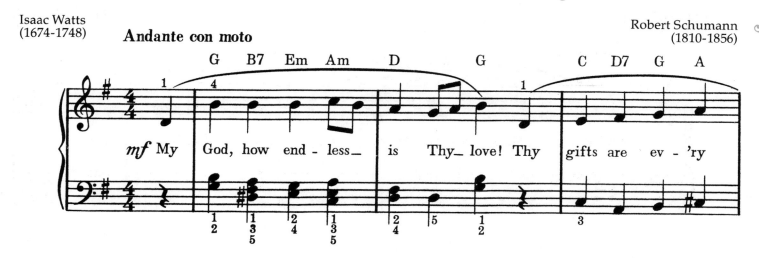

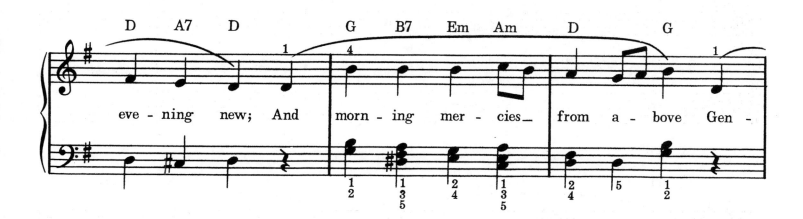

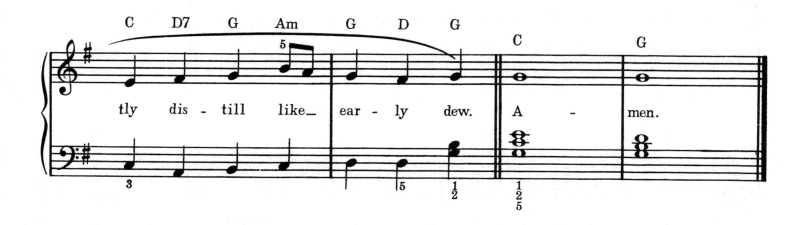

2. Thou spread'st the curtains of the night,
   Great Guardian of my sleeping hours;
   Thy sovereign word restores the light,
   And quickens all my waking powers.

3. I yield my powers to Thy command,
   To Thee I consecrate my days;
   Perpetual blessings from Thy hand
   Demand perpetual songs of praise.

Glorious Things of Thee Are Spoken

John Newton
(1725-1807)

Franz Joseph Haydn
(1732-1809)

2. See, the streams of living waters,
   Springing from eternal love,
   Well supply thy sons and daughters,
   And all fear of want remove.
   Who can faint, when such a river
   Ever will their thirst assuage?
   Grace which, like the Lord, the giver,
   Never fails from age to age.

3. Round each habitation hov'ring,
   See the cloud and fire appear
   For a glory and cov'ring,
   Showing that the Lord is near.
   Safe they feed upon the manna,
   Which He gives them when they pray.
   Thus deriving from their banner,
   Light by night, and shade by day.

(WP41)

Let Us With a Gladsome Mind

John Milton
(1608-1674)

from a 13th Century French Melody
in "The Parish Choir," 1850

2. Let us sound His name abroad,
   For of Gods He is the God
   For His mercies shall endure,
   Ever faithful, ever sure.

3. He, with all-commanding might,
   Filled the new-made world with Light:
   For His mercies shall endure,
   Ever faithful, ever sure.

4. All Things living He doth feed;
   His full hand supplies their need:
   For His mercies shall endure,
   Ever faithful, ever sure.

5. Let us then with gladsome mind
   Praise the Lord, for He is kind;
   For His mercies shall endure,
   Ever faithful, ever sure.

Come, Christians, Join to Sing

Christian H. Bateman
(1813-1889)

Spanish Hymn

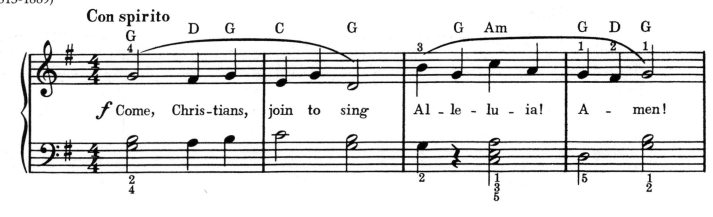

Come, Chris-tians, join to sing   Al - le - lu - ia!   A - men!

Loud   praise to   Christ our King;   Al - le - lu - ia!   A - men!

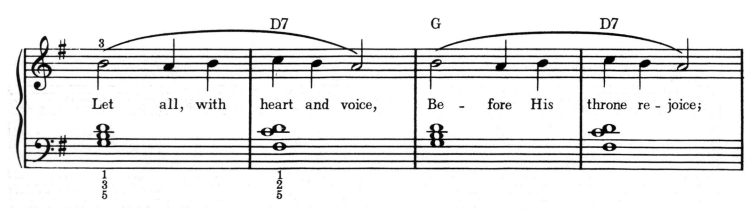

Let   all, with   heart and voice,   Be - fore His   throne re - joice;

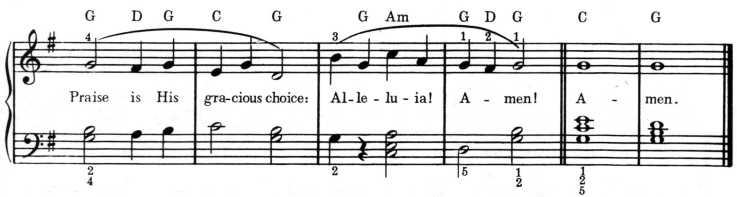

Praise   is His   gra-cious choice: Al - le - lu - ia!   A - men!   A - men.

2. Come, lift your ears on high; Alleluia!
   Amen!
   Let praises fill the sky; Alleluia! Amen!
   He is our Guide and Friend; To us He'll
   condescend;
   His love shall never end; Alleluia! Amen!

3. Praise yet our Christ again; Alleluia!
   Amen!
   Life shall not end the strain; Alleluia!
   Amen!
   On heaven's blissful shore His goodness
   we'll adore,
   Singing forevermore, "Alleluia! Amen!"

Glory Be to the Father
(Gloria Patri)

Source Unknown, 2nd Century

Henry W. Greatorex
(1813-1858)

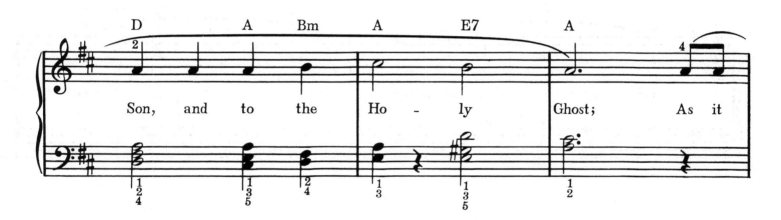

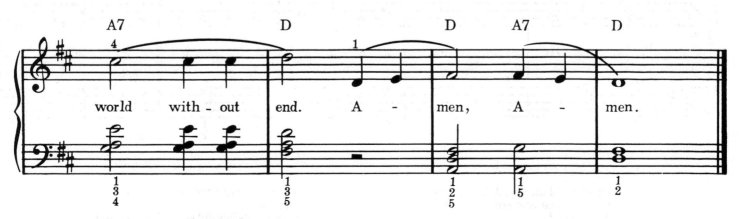

God, That Madest Earth and Heaven

Reginald Heber
(1783-1826)

Traditional Welsh Air

Holy, Holy, Holy!

Reginald Heber
(1783-1826)

John B. Dykes
(1823-1876)

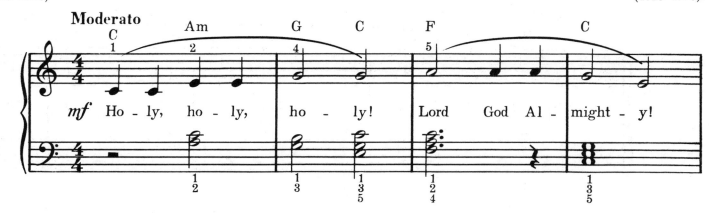

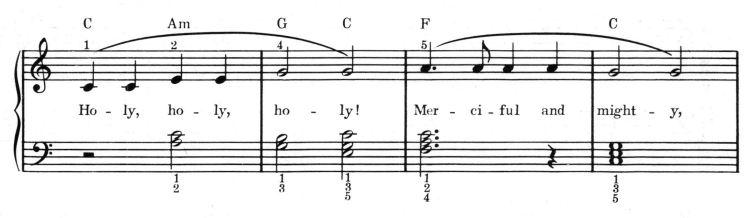

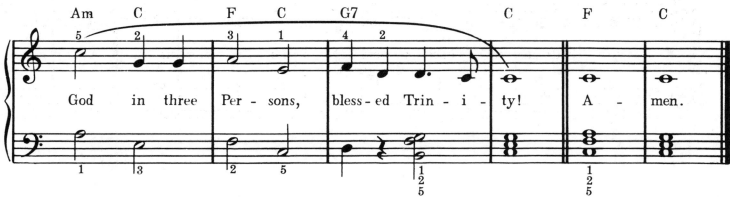

2. Holy, holy, holy! All the saints adore
Thee,
Casting down their golden crowns
around the glassy sea;
Cherubim and seraphim falling down
before Thee,
Who wert, and art, and evermore
shalt be.

3. Holy, holy, holy! Through the darkness
hide Thee,
Though the eye of sinful man Thy glory
may not see,
Only Thou art holy; there is none beside
Thee
Perfect in power, in love, and purity.

4. Holy, holy, holy! Lord God almighty!
All Thy works shall praise Thy name, in
earth and sky and sea;
Holy, holy, holy! Merciful and mighty!
God in three Persons, blessed Trinity!

Beneath the Cross of Jesus

Elizabeth C. Clephane
(1830-1869)

Frederick C. Maker
(1844-1927)

2. Upon the cross of Jesus
Mine eye at times can see
The very dying form of One
Who suffered there for me:
And from my stricken heart with tears
Two wonders I confess:
The wonders of redeeming love
And my unworthiness.

3. I take, O cross, thy shadow
For my abiding place:
I ask no other sunshine than
The sunshine of His face:
Content to let the world go by,
To know no gain nor loss:
My sinful self my only shame,
My glory all the cross.

(WP41)

The King of Love My Shepherd Is

Henry W. Baker
(1821-1877)

John B. Dykes
(1823-1876)

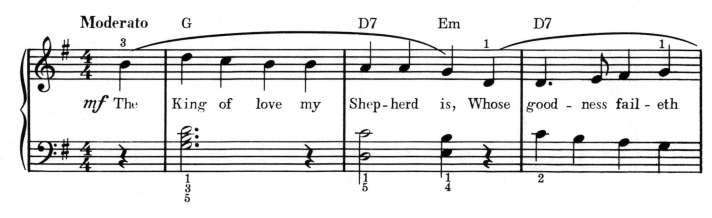

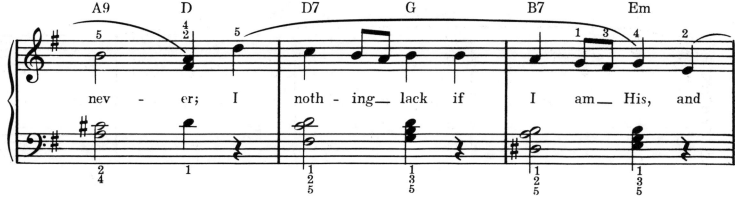

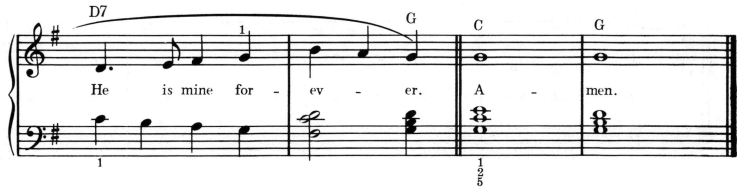

2. Where streams of living water flow
   My ransomed soul He leadeth,
   And where the verdant pastures grow,
   With food celestial feedeth.

3. Perverse and foolish, oft I strayed,
   But yet in love He sought me,
   And on His shoulder gently laid,
   And home, rejoicing, brought me.

4. In death's dark vale I fear no ill
   With Thee, dear Lord, beside me;
   Thy rod and staff my comfort still,
   Thy cross before to guide me.

5. And so through all the length of days
   Thy goodness faileth never:
   Good Shepherd, may I sing Thy praise
   Within Thy house forever.

All Glory, Laud and Honor

Theodulph of Orleans
(760-821)
Translated by John M. Neale
(1818-1866)

Melchior Teschner
(1584-1635)

Maestoso

mf All glo-ry, land and hon - or To Thee, Re-deem-er, King, To

Whom the lips of chil - dren Made sweet ho - san - nas ring! The

peo - ple of the He - brews, With palms be - fore Thee went; Our

praise and prayer and an - thems Be - fore Thee we pre - sent. A - men.

2. Thou art the King of Israel,
Thou David's royal Son,
Who in the Lord's name comest,
The King and blessed One!
To Thee, before Thy passion,
They sang their hymns of praise;
To Thee, on high exalted,
Our melody we raise.

3. Thou didst accept their praises;
Accept the prayers we bring,
Who in all good delightest,
Thou good and gracious King!
All glory, laud and honor
To Thee, Redeemer, King,
To Whom the lips of children
Made sweet hosannas ring!

Crown Him with Many Crowns

Matthew Bridges
(1800-1894)
Godfrey Thring
(1823-1903) Stanza 3

George J. Elvey
(1816-1893)

Maestoso

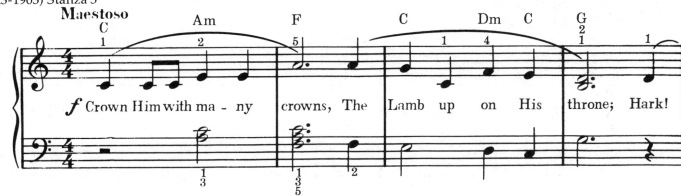

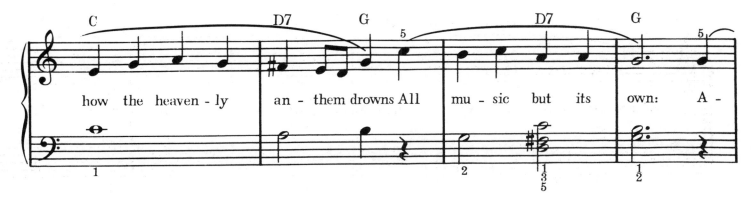

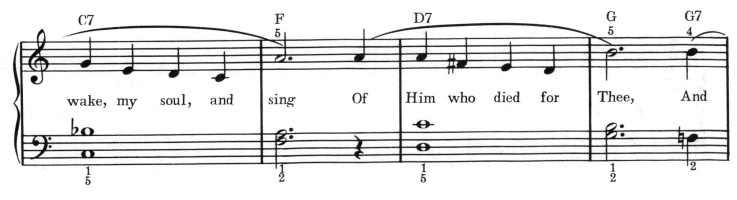

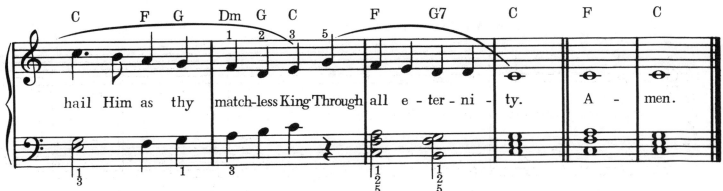

2. Crown Him the Son of God
Before the worlds began,
And ye, who tread where He hath trod,
Crown Him the Son of man;
Who every grief hath known
That wrings the human breast,
And takes and bears them for His own,
That all in Him may rest.

3. Crown Him the Lord of life,
Who triumphed o'er the grave,
And rose victorious in the strife
For those He came to save;
His glories now we sing
Who died, and rose on high
Who died, eternal life to bring,
And lives that death may die.

4. Crown Him the Load of peace,
Whose power a scepter sways
From pole to pole, that wars may cease,
Absorbed in prayer and praise.
His reign shall know no end,
And round His pierced feet
Fair flower of paradise extend
Their fragrance ever sweet.

(WP41)

God of Our Fathers
(National Hymn)

Daniel C. Roberts
(1841-1907)

George W. Warren
(1828-1902)

Maestoso

f

(*Trumpet fanfare, before each stanza*)

God of our fa - thers,

Whose al-might - y hand

Leads forth in beau - ty all the star - ry

band

Of shin - ing worlds in splen-dor through the skies,

Our grate - ful songs be - fore Thy throne a - rise. A - men.

2. Thy love divine hath led us in the past;
   In this free land by Thee our lot is cast;
   Be Thou our ruler, guardian, guide, and stay;
   Thy word our law, Thy paths our chosen way.

3. From war's alarms, from deadly pestilence,
   Be Thy strong arm our ever sure defense;
   Thy true religion in our hearts increase,
   Thy bounteous goodness nourish us in peace.

4. Refresh Thy people on their toilsome way,
   Lead us from night to never-ending day;
   Fill all our lives with love and grace divine,
   And glory, laud, and praise be ever Thine.

Love Divine, All Loves Excelling

Charles Wesley
(1707-1788)

John Zundel
(1815-1882)

Lord di-vine, all loves ex-cel-ling, Joy of heav'n, to earth come down;

Fix in us Thy hum-ble dwell-ing, All Thy faith-ful mer-cies crown!

Je-sus, Thou art all com-pas-sion, Pure, un-bound-ed love Thou art;

Vis-it us with Thy sal-va-tion, En-ter ev'-ry trem-bling heart. A - men.

2. Breathe, O breath Thy loving spirit
   Into every troubled breast!
   Let us all in Thee inherit,
   Let us find the promised rest;
   Take away the love of sinning;
   Alpha and Omega be;
   End of faith, as its beginning,
   Set our hearts at liberty.

3. Come, Almighty to deliver,
   Let us all Thy life receive;
   Suddenly return, and never,
   Nevermore Thy temples leave.
   Thee we would be always blessing,
   Serve Thee as Thy hosts above;
   Pray, and praise Thee without ceasing,
   Glory in Thy perfect love.

4. Finish, then, Thy new creation;
   Pure and spotless let us be;
   Let us see Thy great salvation
   Perfectly restored in Thee;
   Changed from glory into glory,
   Till in heaven we take our place,
   Till we cast our crowns before Thee,
   Lost in wonder, love, and praise.

(WP41)

A Mighty Fortress is Our God

Martin Luther
(1483-1546)
Translated by Frederick H. Hedge
(1805-1890)

Martin Luther
(1483-1546)

(WP41)

GOSPEL, SPIRITUAL, AND FOLK HYMNS

Just a Closer Walk with Thee

Traditional Gospel Hymn

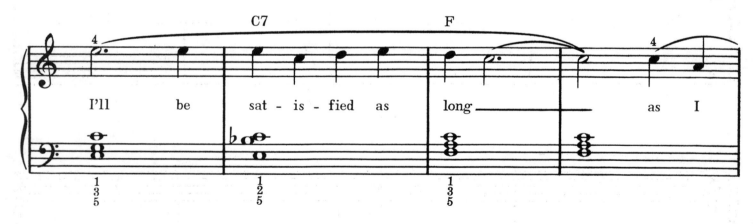

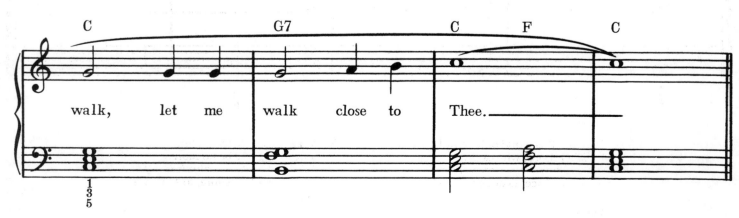

(WP41)

Refrain

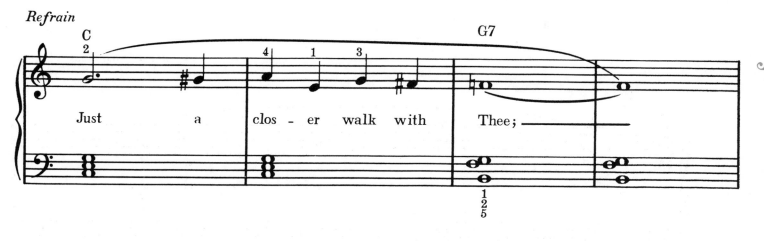

Just   a   clos - er   walk with   Thee; ____

Grant   it   Je - sus,   is   my   plea. ____

Dai - ly   walk - ing close to   Thee, ____   Let   it

be,   dear   Lord,   let   it   be. ____

2. Through this world of toils and snares,
   If I falter, Lord, who cares;
   Who with me my burden shares?
   None but Thee, dear Lord, none but
     Thee:
   Refrain:

3. When my feeble life is o'er,
   Time for me will be no more;
   Guide me gently, safely o'er
   To Thy kingdom shore, to Thy shore.
   Refrain:

Amazing Grace

John Newton

Early American Melody
(1725-1807)

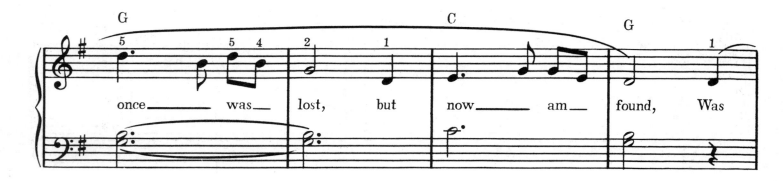

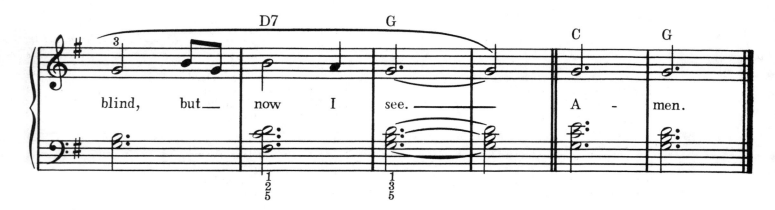

2. 'Twas grace that taught my heart to fear,
   And grace my fears relieved;
   How precious did that grace appear
   The hour I first believed!

3. Through many dangers, toils, and snares,
   I have already come:
   'Tis grace has brought me safe thus far,
   And grace will lead me home.

4. The Lord has promised good to me,
   His word my hope secures;
   He will my shield and portion be
   As long as life endures.

What a Friend We Have in Jesus

Joseph Scriven
(1819-1886)

Charles C. Converse
(1832-1918)

2. Have we trials and temptations?
   Is there trouble anywhere?
   We should never be discouraged,
   Take it to the Lord in prayer!
   Can we find a friend so faithful?
   Who will all our sorrows share?
   Jesus knows our every weakness;
   Take it to the Lord in prayer!

3. Are we weak and heavy-laden,
   Cumbered with a load of care.
   Precious Saviour, still our refuge,
   Take it to the Lord in prayer!
   Do thy friends despise, forsake thee?
   Take it to the Lord in prayer!
   In His arms He'll take and shield thee;
   Thou wilt find a solace there.

He Leadeth Me

Joseph H. Gilmore
(1834-1918)

William B. Bradbury
(1816-1868)

2. Sometimes 'mid scenes of deepest gloom,
Sometimes where Eden's bowers bloom,
By waters still, o'er troubled sea,
Still 'tis His hand that leadeth me.
Refrain:

3. Lord, I would clasp my hand in Thine,
Nor ever murmur nor repine;
Content, whatever lot I see,
Since 'tis my God that leadeth me.
Refrain:

4. And when my task on earth is done,
When, by Thy grace, the victory's won,
E'en death's cold wave I will not flee,
Since God through Jordan leadeth me.
Refrain:

Shall We Gather At the River?

Roberty Lowry
(1826-1899)

Robert Lowry
(1826-1899)

2. On the margin of the river,
   Washing up its silver spray,
   We shall walk and worship ever,
   All the happy golden day.
   Refrain:

3. 'Ere we reach the shining river,
   Lay we every burden down;
   Grace our spirits will deliver,
   And provide a robe and crown.
   Refrain:

4. Soon we'll reach the shining river,
   Soon our pilgrimage will cease;
   Soon our happy hearts will quiver
   With the melody of peace.
   Refrain:

Just As I Am

Charlotte Elliott
(1789-1871)

William B. Bradbury
(1816-1868)

2. Just as I am, and waiting not
   To rid my soul, of one dark blot.
   To Thee, whose blood can cleanse
      each spot,
   O Lamb of God, I come! I come!

3. Just as I am, though tossed about
   With many a conflict, many a doubt.
   Fightings and fears within, without,
   O Lamb of God, I come! I come!

4. Just as I am, poor, wretched, blind,
   Sight, riches, healing of the mind,
   Yes, all I need, in Thee I find,
   O Lamb of God, I come! I come!

5. Just as I am, Thou wilt receive,
   Wilt welcome, pardon, cleanse, relieve,
   Because Thy promise I believe,
   O Lamb of God, I come! I come!

6. Just as I am, Thy love unknown
   Hath broken every barrier down;
   Now, to be Thine, yea, Thine alone,
   O Lamb of God, I come! I come!

(WP41)

Bringing in the Sheaves

Knowles Shaw

George A. Minor
(1834-1878)

(WP41)

Battle Hymn of the Republic

Julia Ward Howe

William Steffe
(1819-1910)

With spirit

mf Mine eyes have seen the glo - ry of the com - ing of the

Lord; He is tram - pling out the vin - tage where the

grapes of wrath are stored; He hath loosed the fate - ful

light - ning of His ter - ri - ble swift sword; His

truth is march - ing on.

(WP41)

Refrain

f Glo - ry! glo - ry! Hal - le - lu - jah!

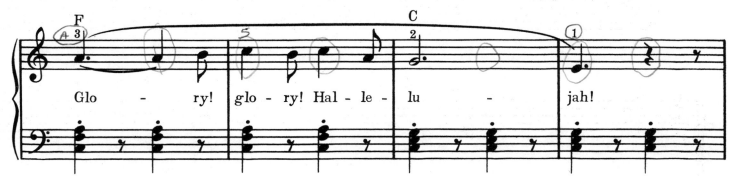

Glo - ry! glo - ry! Hal - le - lu - jah!

Glo - ry! glo - ry! Hal - le - lu - jah! His

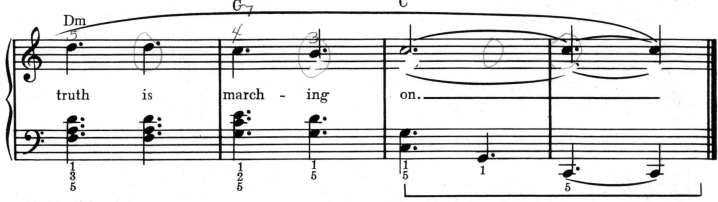

truth is march - ing on.

2. I have seen Him in the watch-fires
   Of a hundred circling camps;
   They have builded Him an altar
   In the evening dews and damps;
   I can read His righteous sentence
   By the dim and flaring lamps;
   His day is marching on.

   Refrain:

3. He has sounded forth the trumpet
   That shall never sound retreat;
   He is sifting out the hearts of men
   Before His judgment seat;
   O be swift, my soul, to answer Him!
   Be jubilant, my feet!
   Our God is marching on.

   Refrain:

4. In the beauty of the lilies,
   Christ was born across the sea,
   With a glory in His bosom
   That transfigures you and me;
   As He died to make men holy,
   Let us die to make men free,
   While God is marching on.

   Refrain:

Beulah Land

Edgar Page Stites

John R. Sweney
(1837-1899)

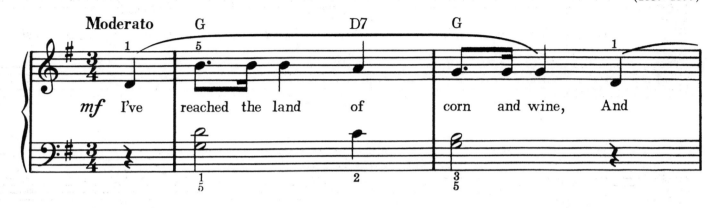

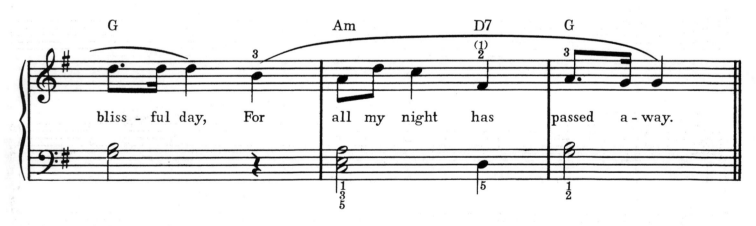

2. My Savior comes and walks with me,
   And sweet communion here have we;
   He gently leads me by His hand,
   For this is heaven's border land.
   Refrain:

3. A sweet perfume upon the breeze
   Is born from ever-vernal trees,
   And flowers that never-fading grow
   Where streams of life forever flow.
   Refrain:

4. The zephyrs seem to float to me
   Sweet sound of heaven's melody,
   As angels with the white-robed throng
   Join in the sweet redemption song.
   Refrain:

Jesus Saves

Priscilla J. Owens
(1829-1907)

William J. Kirkpatrick
(1838-1921)

We have heard the joy-ful sound: Je - sus saves! Je - sus saves! Spread the ti - dings all a - round: Je - sus saves! Je - sus saves! Bear the news to eve - ry land, Climb the steeps and cross the waves; On-ward! 'tis our Lord's com - mand; Je - sus saves! Je - sus saves!

2. Waft it on the rolling tide;
Jesus saves! Jesus saves!
Tell to sinners far and wide:
Jesus saves! Jesus saves!
Sing, ye islands of the sea:
Echo back, ye ocean caves;
Earth shall keep her jubilee:
Jesus saves! Jesus saves!

3. Give the winds a mighty voice,
Jesus saves! Jesus saves!
Let the nations now rejoice,
Jesus saves! Jesus saves!
Shout salvation full and free
Highest hills and deepest caves;
This our song of victory:
Jesus saves! Jesus saves!

(WP41)

Work, for the Night Is Coming

Anna L. Coghill
(1836-1907)

Lowell Mason
(1792-1872)

Moderato

mf Work, for the night is com - ing; Work through the morn-ing hours;

Work while the dew is spark - ling; Work 'mid spring - ing flowers;

Work when the day grows bright - er; Work in the glow - ing sun;

Work, for the night is com - ing, When man's work is done.

2. Work, for the night is coming;
Work in the sunny noon;
Fill brightest hours with labor:
Rest comes sure and soon.
Give every flying minute
Something to keep in store;
Work, for the night is coming,
When man works no more.

3. Work, for the night is coming,
Under the sunset skies;
While their bright tints are glowing,
Work, for daylight flies.
Work till the last beam fadeth,
Fadeth to shine no more;
Work while the night is darkening.
When man's work is o'er.

Jesus, Keep Me Near the Cross

Fanny Crosby
(1820-1915)

William H. Doane
(1832-1915)

Moderato

mf Je - sus, keep me near the cross; There a pre - cious foun - tain,

Free to all, a heal - ing stream, Flows from Cal - vary's moun - tain.

Refrain

In the cross, in the cross, Be my glo - ry ev - er,

Till my rap-tured soul shall find Rest be-yond the riv - er. A - men.

2. Near the cross, a trembling soul,
Love and mercy found me;
There the bright and morning Star
Shed His beams around me.
Refrain:

3. Near the cross! O Lamb of God,
Bring its scenes before me;
Help me walk from day to day
With its shadow o'er me.
Refrain:

4. Near the cross I'll watch and wait,
Hoping, trusting ever,
Till I reach the golden strand,
Just beyond the river.
Refrain:

(WP41)

I've Found a Friend

James G. Small
(1817-1888)

James Bastien

2. I've found a Friend, O such a Friend!
   He bled, He died to save me;
   And not alone the gift of life,
   But His own self He gave me!
   Nought that I have mine own I call,
   I'll hold it for the giver,
   My heart, my strength, my life, my all
   Are His, and His forever.

3. I've found a Friend, O such a Friend!
   So kind and true and tender,
   So wise a Counselor and Guide,
   So mighty a Defender!
   From Him who loves me now so well
   What power my soul can sever?
   Shall life or death, shall earth or hell?
   No! I am His forever.

(WP41)

Beautiful Isle of Somewhere

Jessie B. Pounds

John S. Fearis

mf Some - where the sun is shin - ing,

Some - where the song - birds dwell; ____

Hush, then, thy sad re - pin - ing,

God lives, and all ____ is well. ____

(WP41)

Refrain

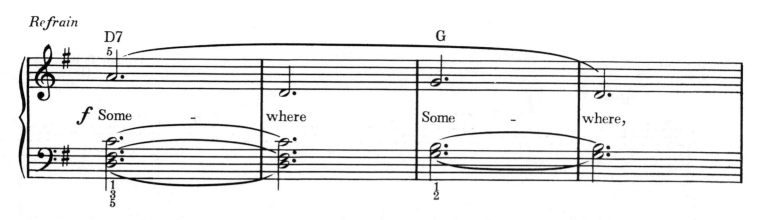

Some — where Some — where,

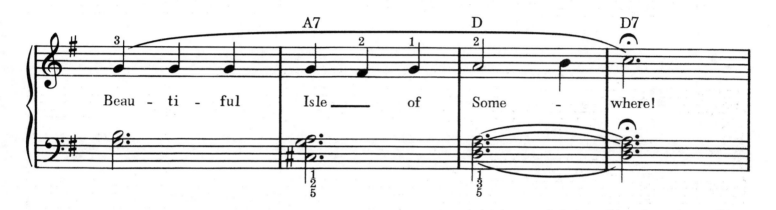

Beau — ti — ful Isle ____ of Some — where!

Land of the true, where we live a — new,

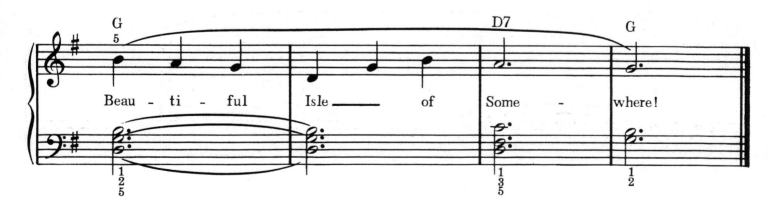

Beau — ti — ful Isle ____ of Some — where!

2. Somewhere the day is longer,
   Somewhere the task is done;
   Somewhere the heart is stronger,
   Somewhere the vict'ries won.
   Refrain:

3. Somewhere the load is lifted,
   Close by an open gate;
   Somewhere the clouds are rifted,
   Somewhere the angels wait.
   Refrain:

Sweet Hour of Prayer

William W. Walford
(1772-1850)

...dbury
(...6-1868)

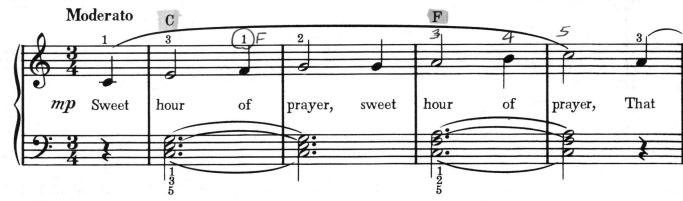

mp Sweet hour of prayer, sweet hour of prayer, That

calls me from ___ a world of care, And

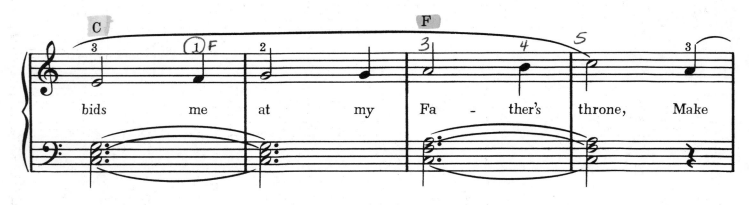

bids me at my Fa - ther's throne, Make

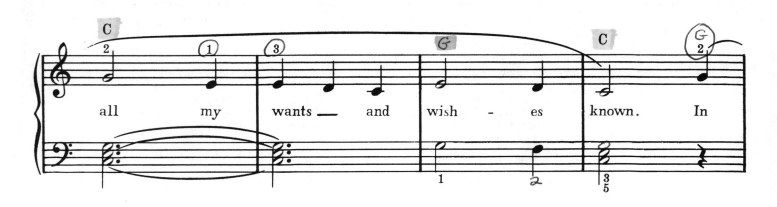

all my wants ___ and wish - es known. In

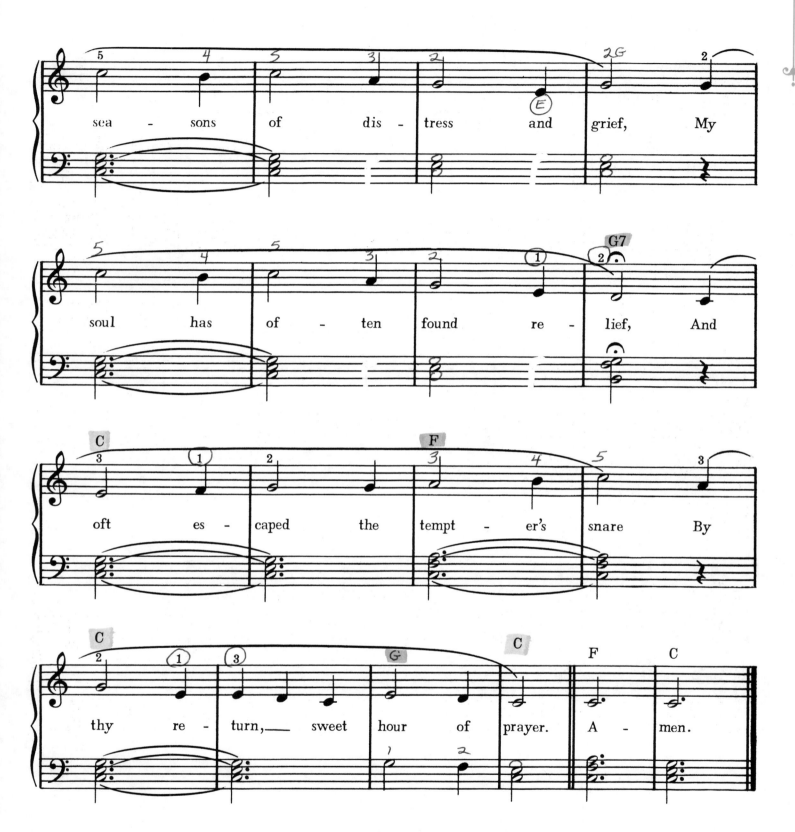

2. Sweet hour of prayer, sweet hour of
   prayer,
   Thy wings shall my petition bear
   To Him whose truth and faithfulness
   Engage the waiting soul to bless;
   And since He bids me seek His face,
   Believe His work, and trust His grace,
   I'll cast on Him my every care
   And wait for thee, sweet hour of prayer.

3. Sweet hour of prayer, sweet hour of
   prayer,
   The joy I feel, the bliss I share
   Of those whose anxious spirits burn
   With strong desire for Thy return.
   With such I hasten to the place
   Where God, my Saviour, shows His face,
   And gladly take my station there
   And wait for thee, sweet hour of prayer.

Softly and Tenderly Jesus is Calling

Will L. Thompson
(1847-1909)

Will L. Thompson
(1847-1909)

Refrain

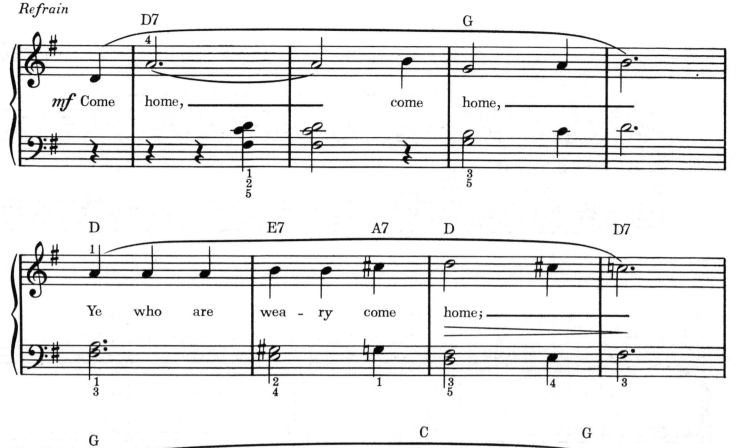

Come home, _____ come home, _____

Ye who are wea-ry come home; _____

mp Ear - nest-ly, ten-der-ly, Je - sus is call - ing,

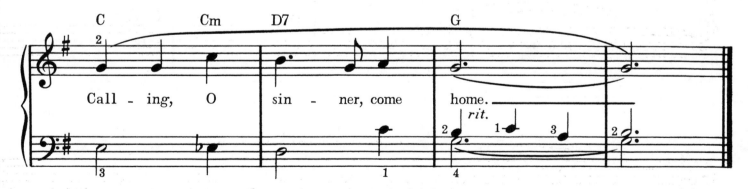

Call - ing, O sin - ner, come home. _____ *rit.*

2. Why should we tarry
When Jesus is pleading,
Pleading for you and for me?
Why should we linger
And heed not His mercies,
Mercies for you and for me.

    Refrain:

3. Time is now fleeting,
The moments are passing,
Passing from you and from me;
Shadows are gathering,
Death's night is coming,
Coming for you and for me.

    Refrain:

4. Oh! For the wonderful
Love He has promised,
Promised for you and for me;
Tho' we have sinned,
He has mercy and pardon,
Pardon for you and for me.

    Refrain:

Joy, Joy, Joy

Traditional Gospel

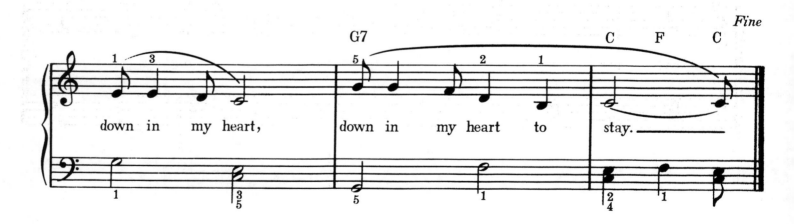

Fine

And it's the grand — est, great — est feel — ing, And it's a

feel — ing here to stay. ———— And it's a joy that needs re —

veal — ing, So I just want to say: ————

In the Sweet By and By

Sanford F. Bennett
(1836-1898)

Joseph P. Webster
(1819-1875)

2. We shall sing on that beautiful shore
   The melodious songs of the blest,
   And our spirits shall sorrow no more,
   Not a sigh for the blessing of rest.
   Refrain:

3. To our bountiful Father above,
   We will offer our tribute of praise,
   For the glorious gift of His love,
   And the blessings that hallow our days.
   Refrain:

Were You There?

Traditional Spiritual

2. Were you there when they nailed Him to
the tree?

3. Were you there when they laid Him in
the tomb?

Give Me That Old Time Religion

Traditional Spiritual

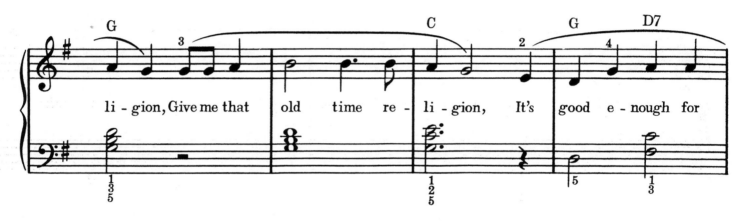

(WP41)

Nobody Knows the Trouble I've Seen

Traditional Spiritual

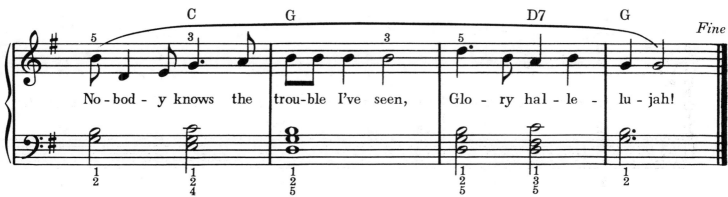

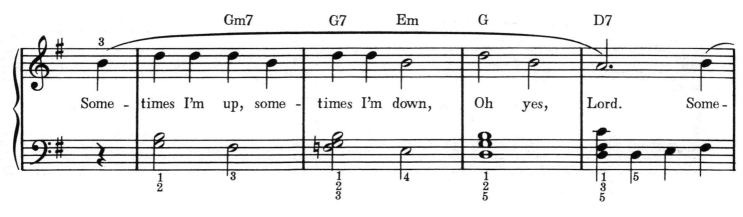

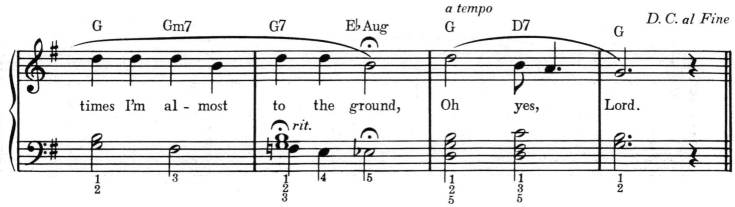

Go Tell It on the Mountain

Traditional Spiritual

(WP41)

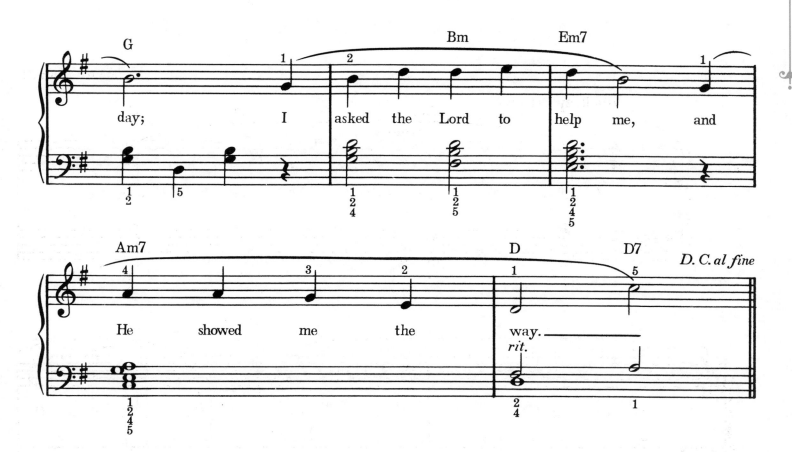

2. When I was a seeker, I sought both night
        and day;
    I asked my Lord to help me, and He
        taught me to pray.

3. He made me a watchman up on the
        city wall;
    And if I am a Christian, I am the least
        of all.

Swing Low, Sweet Chariot

Traditional Spiritual

Steal Away

Traditional Spiritual

Slowly, with expression

When the Saints Go Marching In

Traditional Spiritual

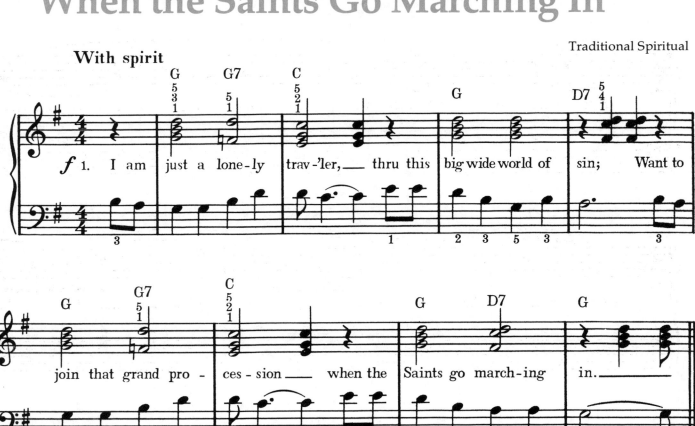

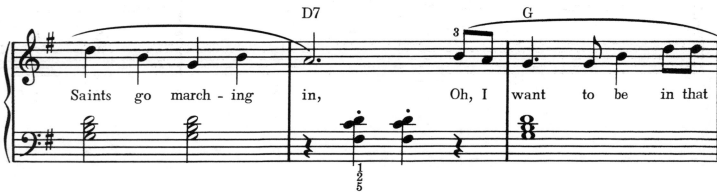

He's Got the Whole World in His Hands

Traditional Spiritual

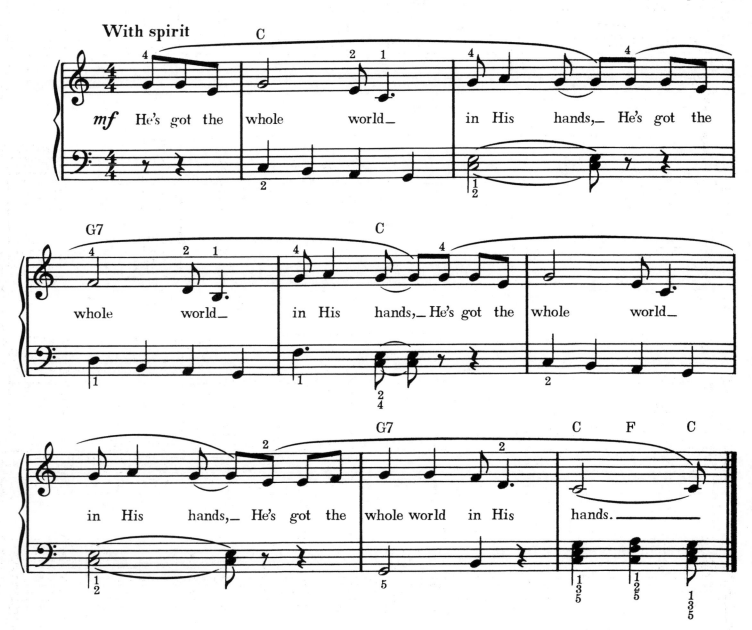

2. He's got the tiny little baby in His
   hands, . . .

3. He's got you and me, brother, in His
   hands, . . .

4. He's got you and me, sister, in His
   hands, . . .

5. He's got everybody in His hands, . . .

Jacob's Ladder

Traditional Spiritual

2. Every round goes higher, higher . . .

3. Brother, do you love my Jesus? . . .

4. If you love Him, you must serve Him, . . .

5. We are climbing higher, higher, . . .

Amen

Traditional Folk Hymn

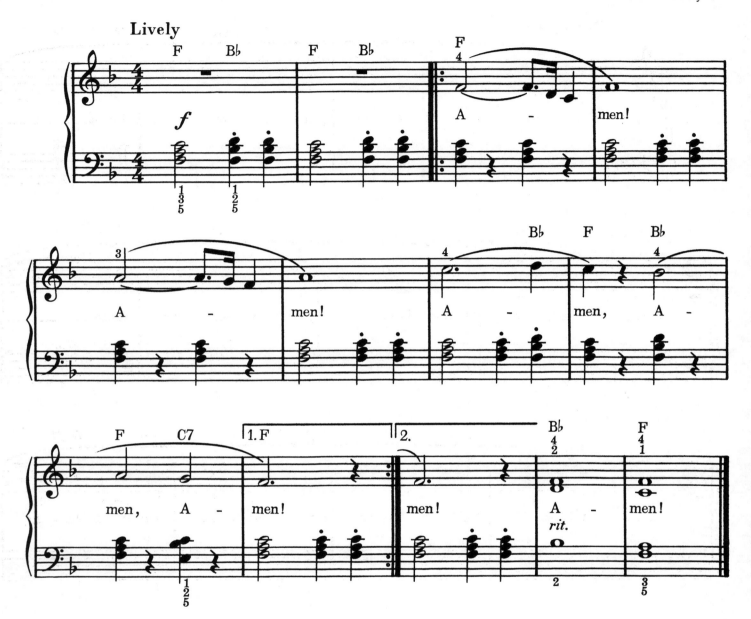

Let Us Break Bread Together

American Folk Hymn

2. Let us drink wine together on our knees.
   Let us drink wine together on our knees.
   When I fall on my knees,
   With my face to the rising sun,
   O Lord, have mercy on me.

3. Let us praise God together on our knees.
   Let us praise God together on our knees.
   When I fall on my knees,
   With my face to the rising sun,
   O Lord, have mercy on me.

Jesus Healing

Kum-Ba-Ya*

African Folk Hymn

*"Kum-Ba-Ya, my Lord" means "Come by here, my Lord."

HYMNS FOR SPECIAL OCCASIONS

(including Thanksgiving, Christmas, Easter and Weddings)

Come, Ye Thankful People, Come

Henry Alford
(1810-1871)

George J. Elvey
(1816-1893)

2. All the world is God's own field,
   Fruit unto His praise to yield;
   Wheat and tares together sown,
   Unto joy or sorrow grown;
   First the blade, and then the ear,
   Then the full corn shall appear:
   Lord of harvest, grant that we
   Wholesome grain and pure may be.

3. For the Lord our God shall come,
   And shall take His harvest home;
   From His field shall in that day
   All offenses purge away;
   Give His angels charge at last
   In the fire the tares to cast;
   But the fruitful ears to store
   In His garner evermore.

4. Even so, Lord, quickly come
   To Thy final harvest-home;
   Gather Thou Thy people in,
   Free from sorrow, free from sin:
   There forever purified,
   In Thy presence to abide;
   Come, with all Thine angels, come,
   Raise the glorious harvest-home.

Now Thank We All Our God

Martin Rinkart
(1586-1649)
Translated by Catherine Winkworth
(1827-1878)

John Cruger
(1598-1662)

2. O, may this bounteous God
Through all our life be near us,
With ever joyful hearts
And blessed peace to cheer us;
And keep us in His grace,
And guide us when perplexed,
And free us from all ills
In this world and the next.

3. All praise and thanks to God
The Father now be given,
The Son, and Him who reigns
With them in highest heaven,
The one eternal God,
Whom earth and heaven adore;
For thus it was, is now,
And shall be evermore.

(WP41)

We Plow the Field and Scatter

Matthias Claudius
(1740-1815)
Translated by Jane M. Campbell
(1817-1878)

Johann A. P. Schulz
(1747-1800)

Refrain

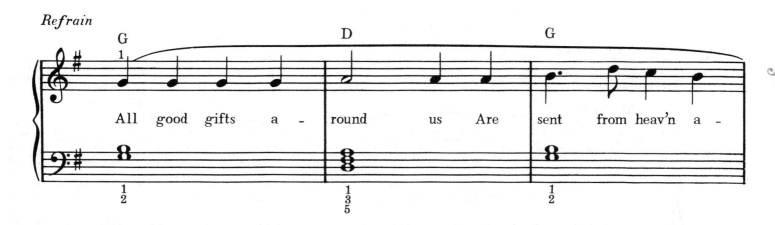

All good gifts a - round us Are sent from heav'n a -

bove; Then thank the Lord, O thank the Lord For

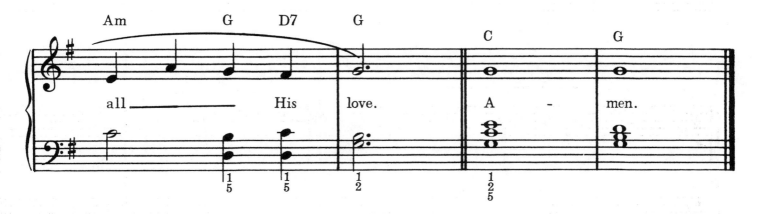

all _____ His love. A - men.

2. He only is the Maker
   Of all things near and far;
   He paints the wayside flower,
   He lights the evening star;
   The winds and waves obey Him,
   By Him the birds are fed;
   Much more to us, His children,
   He gives our daily bread.
   Refrain:

3. We thank Thee, then, O Father,
   For all things bright and good,
   The seedtime and the harvest,
   Our life, our health, our food:
   Accept the gifts we offer
   For all Thy love imparts,
   And what Thou most desirest,
   Our humble, thankful hearts.
   Refrain:

Sing To the Lord of Harvest

John S. B. Monsell
(1811-1875)

Henry Smart
(1813-1879)

2. By Him the clouds drop richness
   The deserts bloom and spring,
   The hills leap up in gladness,
   The valleys laugh and sing;
   He filleth with His fullness
   All things with large increase;
   He crowns the year with goodness,
   With plenty and with peace.

3. Heap on His sacred altar
   The gifts His goodness gave,
   The golden sheaves of harvest,
   The souls He died to save;
   Your hearts lay down before Him
   When at His feet you fall,
   And with your lives adore Him
   Who gave His life for all.

4. To God, the gracious Father,
   Who made us very good,
   To Christ, who, when we wandered,
   Restored us with His blood,
   And to the Holy Spirit,
   Who does upon us pour
   His blessed dews and sunshine,
   Be praise forevermore.

(WP41)

Away in a Manger

James R. Murray
(1841-1905)

Andante con moto

mp A - way in a man - ger, no crib for His bed, The
lit - tle Lord Je - sus laid down His sweet head; The
stars in the sky looked down where He lay, The
lit - tle Lord Je - sus, a - sleep on the hay.

2. The cattle are lowing, the Baby wakes,
   But little Lord Jesus, no crying He makes.
   I love Thee, Lord Jesus, look down from
      the sky,
   And stay by my cradle till morning is
      nigh.

3. Be near me, Lord Jesus, I ask Thee to stay
   Close by me forever, and love me I pray.
   Bless all the dear children in Thy tender
      care,
   And fit us for Heaven, to live with Thee
      there.

Joy to the World

Isaac Watts
(1674-1748)
Adapted by Lowell Mason
(1792-1872)

Handel
(-1759)

With spirit

f Joy to the world! the Lord is come; Let

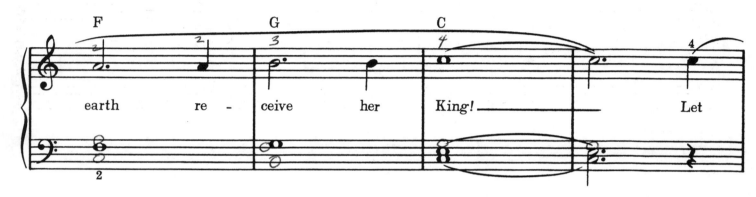

earth re - ceive her King! Let

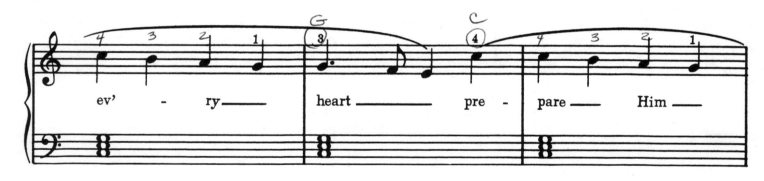

ev' - ry heart pre - pare Him

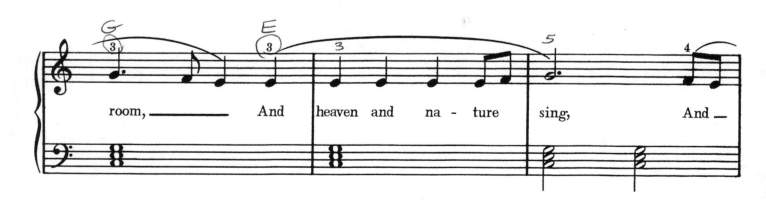

room, And heaven and na - ture sing, And

(WP41)

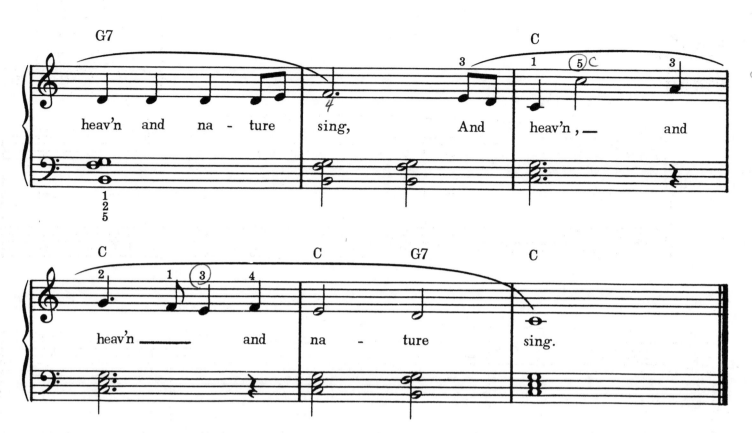

2. Joy to the world! The Saviour reigns;
   Let men their songs employ;
   While fields and floods, rocks, hills and
      plains
   Repeat the sounding joy,
   Repeat the sounding joy,
   Repeat, repeat the sounding joy.

3. No more let sins and sorrows grow,
   Nor thorns infest the ground;
   He comes to make His blessings flow
   Far as the curse is found,
   Far as the curse is found,
   Far as, far as the curse is found.

4. He rules the world with truth and grace
   And makes the nations prove
   The glories of His righteousness,
   And wonders of His love,
   And wonders of His love,
   And wonders, wonders of His love.

The First Noel

English Carol

mf The first Noel, the an-gel did say, Was to

cer - tain poor shep-herds in fields as they lay; In

fields where they lay keep-ing their sheep, On a

cold win-ter's night that was so deep.

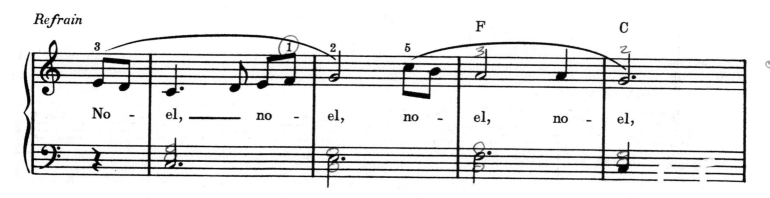

Refrain

Noel, —— no - el, no - el, no - el,

Born is the King —— of Is - ra - el.

2. They looked up and saw a star
   Shining in the east, beyond them far,
   And to the earth it gave great light,
   And so it continued both day and night.
   Refrain:

3. And by the light of that same star,
   Three wise men came from country far;
   To seek for a King was their intent,
   And to follow the star wherever it went.
   Refrain:

4. This star drew nigh to the northwest,
   O'er Bethlehem it took its rest,
   And there it did both stop and stay,
   Right over the place where Jesus lay.
   Refrain:

5. Then entered in those wise men three,
   Full rev'rently upon the knee,
   And offered there, in His presence,
   Their gold, and myrrh, and frankincense.
   Refrain:

6. Then let us all with one accord
   Sing praises to our heav'nly Lord,
   That hath made heav'n and earth of
      naught,
   And with His blood mankind hath
      bought.
   Refrain:

Hark! The Herald Angels Sing

Felix Mendelssohn
(1809-1847)

2

(WP41)

Angels We Have Heard on High

Old French Carol

Moderato

mf An-gels we have heard on high, Sweet-ly sing-ing o'er the plains;

And the moun-tains in re-ply, Ech-o back their joy-ous strains.

Refrain

f Glo - - - - ri - a

in ex-cel-sis De-o, Glo - -

- - ri-a in ex-cel-sis De - o.

2. Shepherds why this jubilee?
   Why your joyous strains prolong
   Say what may the tidings be,
   Which inspire your heavenly song?
   Refrain:

3. Come to Bethlehem and see,
   Him whose birth the angels sing;
   Come adore on bended knee,
   Christ, the Lord, our newborn King.
   Refrain:

(WP41)

Silent Night

Franz Grüber

Si - lent night, Ho - ly night,

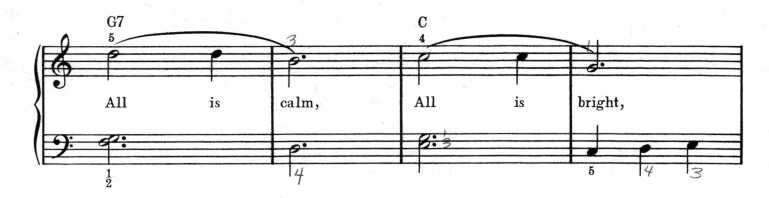

All is calm, All is bright,

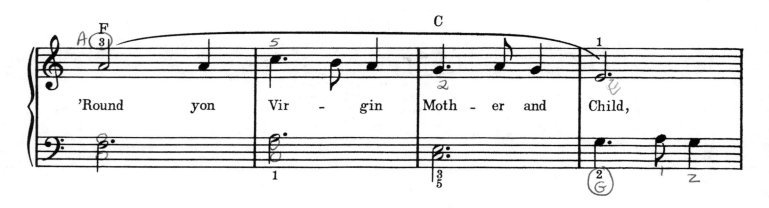

'Round yon Vir - gin Moth - er and Child,

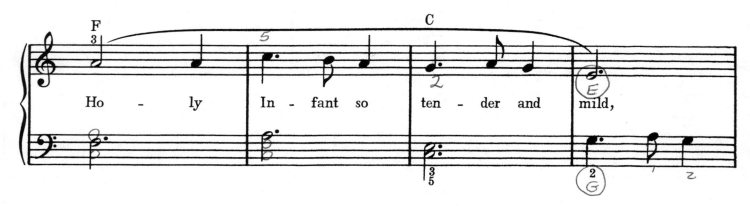

Ho - ly In - fant so ten - der and mild,

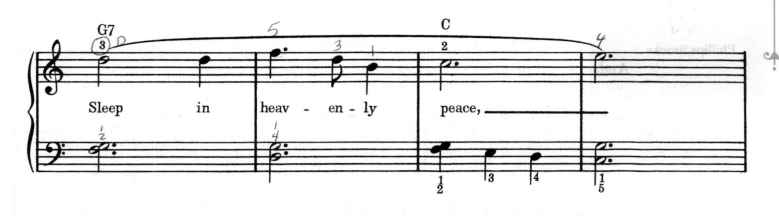

Sleep in heav - en - ly peace, _____

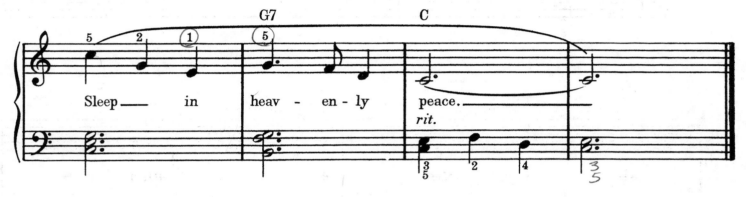

Sleep ___ in heav - en - ly peace. _____

rit.

2. Silent night, Holy night,
   Shepherds quake at the sight;
   Glories stream from heaven afar,
   Heavenly hosts sing Alleluia,
   Christ, the Saviour, is born!
   Christ, the Saviour, is born!

3. Silent night, Holy night,
   Son of God, love's pure light
   Radiant beams from Thy holy face,
   With the dawn of redeeming grace,
   Jesus, Lord, at Thy birth,
   Jesus, Lord, at Thy birth.

O Little Town of Bethlehem

Lewis H. Redner

Birth of Jesus

2. How silently, how silently,
   The wondrous gift is given!
   So God imparts to human hearts
   The blessings of his heaven.
   No ear may hear his coming,
   But in this world of sin,
   Where meek souls will receive Him,
   Still dear Christ enters in.

3. O Holy Child of Bethlehem,
   Descend to us, we pray;
   Cast out our sin, and enter in,
   Be born in us today.
   We hear the Christmas angels
   The great glad tidings tell;
   O come to us, abide with us,
   Our Lord Immanuel!

O Come, All Ye Faithful

from John F. Wade's "Cantus Diversi"
(1751)

Jesus Christ is Risen Today

Stanzas 1 to 3, based on the Latin, 14th Century
Stanza 4, Charles Wesley (1707-1788)

From "Lyra Davidica"
(1708)

Je-sus Christ is risen to-day,— Al - le - lu - ia!

Our tri-um-phant ho-ly day,— Al - le - lu - ia!

Who did once, up - on the cross, Al - le - lu - ia!

Suf - fer — to re - deem our loss.— Al - le - lu - ia!

2. Hymns of praise then let us sing, Alleluia!
Unto Christ, our heavenly King, Alleluia!
Who endured the cross and grave,
Alleluia!
Sinners to redeem and save. Alleluia!

3. But the pains which He endured,
Alleluia!
Our salvation have procured; Alleluia!
Now above the sky He's King, Alleluia!
Where the angels ever sing. Alleluia!

4. Sing we to our God above, Alleluia!
Praise eternal as His love; Alleluia!
Praise Him all ye heavenly host, Alleluia!
Father, Son, and Holy Ghost. Alleluia!

(WP41)

Come, Ye Faithful, Raise the Strain

St. John of Damascus

Arthur S. Sullivan

2. Tis the Spring of souls today;
   Christ hath burst His prison,
   And from three days sleep in death
   As a sun hath risen;
   All the winter of our sins,
   O long and dark, is flying
   From His light, to whom we give
   Laud and praise undying.

3. Now the queen of season, bright
   With the day of splendor,
   With the royal feast of feasts,
   Comes its joy to render;
   Comes to glad Jerusalem,
   Who with true affection
   Welcomes in unwearied strains
   Jesus' resurrection.

4. Neither might the gates of death,
   Nor the tomb's dark portals,
   Nor the watchers, nor the seal,
   Hold Thee as a mortal;
   But today amidst the Twelve
   Thou didst stand, bestowing
   That Thy peace, which evermore
   Passeth human knowing.

The Strife is O'er

Translated by Frances Pott

Giovanni Palestrina
Adapted by William H. Monk

2. The bowers of death have done their
   worst;
   But Christ their legions hath dispersed:
   Let shouts of holy joy outburst
   Alleluia!

3. The three sad days are quickly sped;
   He rises glorious from the dead:
   All glory to our risen Head!
   Alleluia!

4. He closed the yawning gates of hell,
   The bars from heaven's high portals fell;
   Let hymns of praise His triumphs tell!
   Alleluia!

5. Lord! by the stripes which wounded
   Thee,
   From death's dread sting Thy servants
   free,
   That we may live and sing to Thee,
   Alleluia!

The Day of Resurrection

John of Damascus

Michael Haydn

2. Our hearts be pure from evil,
   That we may see aright
   The Lord in rays eternal
   Of resurrection light;
   And, listening to his accents,
   May hear so calm and plain
   His own "All hail," and, hearing,
   May raise the victor strain.

3. Now let the heavens be joyful,
   Let earth her song begin,
   The round world keep high triumph,
   And all that is therein;
   Let all things seen and unseen
   Their notes together blend,
   For Christ the Lord is risen,
   Our joy that hath no end.

O Perfect Love

Dorothy F. Gurney

Sir John Barnby

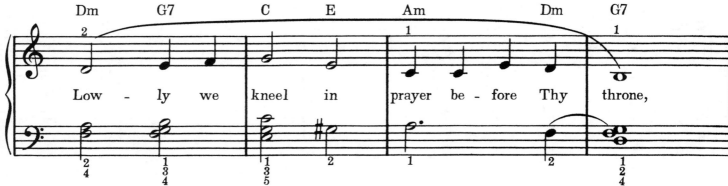

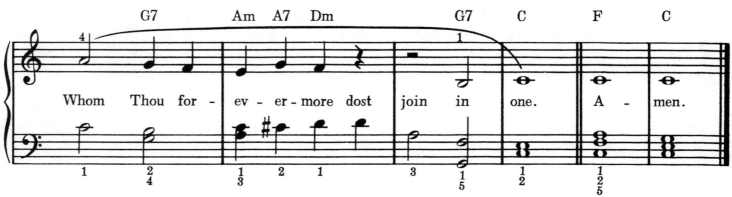

2. O perfect Life, be Thou their full
      assurance
   Of tender charity and steadfast faith,
   Of patient hope, and quiet, brave
      endurance,
   With childlike trust that fears nor pain
      nor death.

3. Grant them the joy which brightens
      earthly sorrow;
   Grant them the peace which calms all
      earthly strife,
   And to life's day the glorious unknown
      morrow
   That dawns upon eternal love and life.

(WP41)

HYMNS FOR CHILDREN

All Things Bright and Beautiful

Cecil F. Alexander
(1818-1895)

William H. Monk
(1823-1889)

(*other verses*)

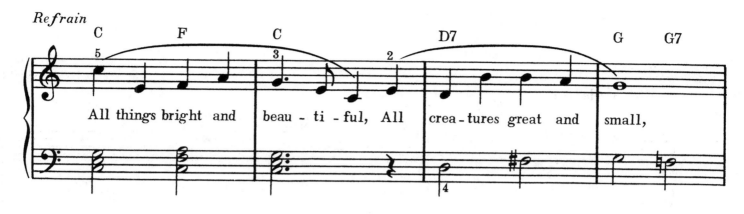

2. The purple-headed mountain,
   The river running by,
   The sunset, and the morning
   That brightens up the sky;
   Refrain:

3. The cold wind in the winter,
   The pleasant summer sun,
   The ripe fruits in the garden,
   He made them every one.
   Refrain:

4. The tall trees in the greenwood,
   The meadows where we play,
   The rushes by the water
   We gather every day.
   Refrain:

5. He gave us eyes to see them,
   And lips that we might tell
   How great is God Almighty,
   Who has made all things well.
   Refrain:

Jesus Loves Me

Anna B. Warner
(1820-1915)

William B. Bradbury
(1816-1868)

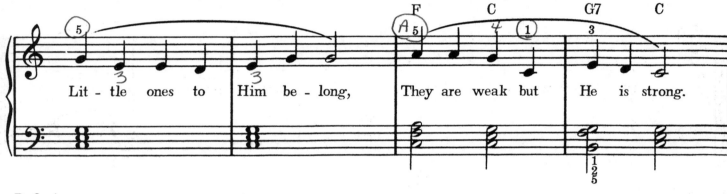

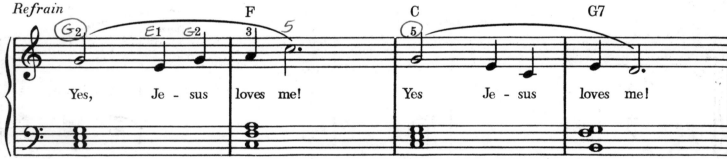

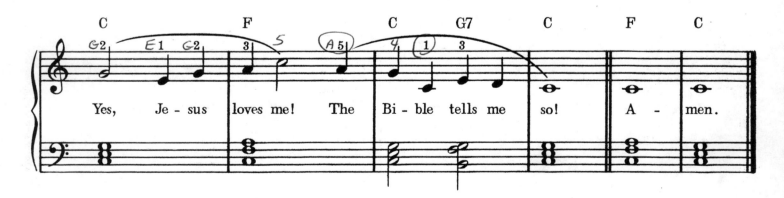

2. Jesus from His throne on high,
   Came into this world to die;
   That I might from sin be free,
   Bled and died upon the tree.
   Refrain:

3. Jesus loves me! He Who died
   Heaven's gates to open wide,
   He will wash away my sin,
   Let His little child come in.
   Refrain:

4. Jesus, take this heart of mine;
   Make it pure, and wholly Thine:
   Thou hast bled and died for me,
   I will henceforth live for Thee.
   Refrain:

Jesus Wants Me for a Sunbeam

Nellie Talbot

E. O. Excell

2. Jesus wants me to be loving
   And kind to all I see,
   Showing how pleasant and happy
   His little one can be.
   Refrain:

3. I will ask Jesus to help me
   To keep my heart from sin,
   Showing how pleasant and happy
   His little one can be.
   Refrain:

4. I'll be a sunbeam for Jesus;
   I can if I but try,
   Serving Him moment by moment,
   Then live with Him on high.
   Refrain:

Little Drops of Water

Julia Carney

French Tune

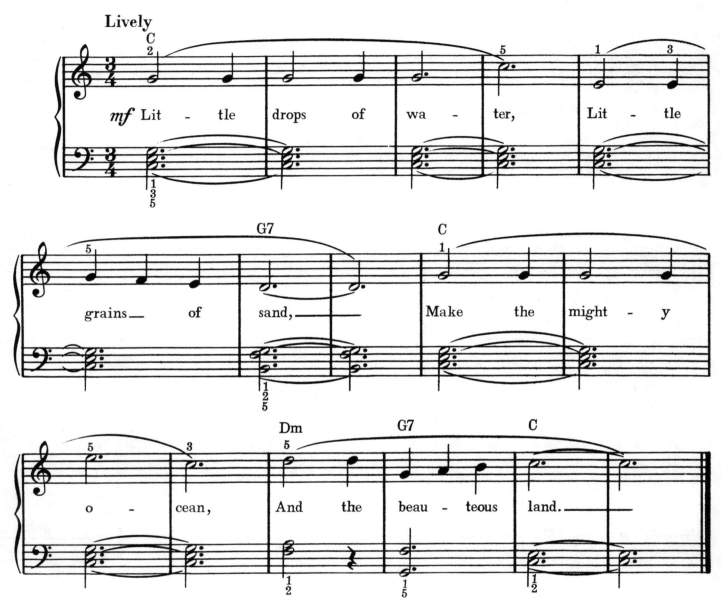

Lit - tle drops of wa - ter, Lit - tle grains of sand, Make the might - y o - cean, And the beau - teous land.

2. And the little moments,
   Humble though they be,
   Make the mighty ages
   Of eternity.

3. So our little errors
   Lead the soul away
   From the paths of virtue
   Oft in sin to stray.

4. Little seeds of mercy,
   Sown by youthful hands,
   Grow to bless the nations,
   Far ir heathen lands.

5. Little deeds of kindness,
   Little words of love,
   Make our earth an Eden,
   Like the Heaven above.

This Is My Father's World

Babcock
(1858-1901)

Traditional English Melody
Adapted by Franklin L. Sheppard
(1852-1930)

2. This is my Father's world:
   The birds their carols raise,
   The morning light, the lily white,
   Declare their Maker's praise.
   This is my Father's world:
   He shines in all that's fair;
   In the rustling grass I hear Him pass,
   He speaks to me everywhere.

3. This is my Father's world:
   Oh, let me ne'er forget
   That though the wrong seems oft so
      strong.
   God is the Ruler yet.
   This is my Father's world:
   The battle is not done;
   Jesus who died shall be satisfied,
   And earth and heaven be one.

Father, We Thank Thee for the Night

Daniel Batcheller

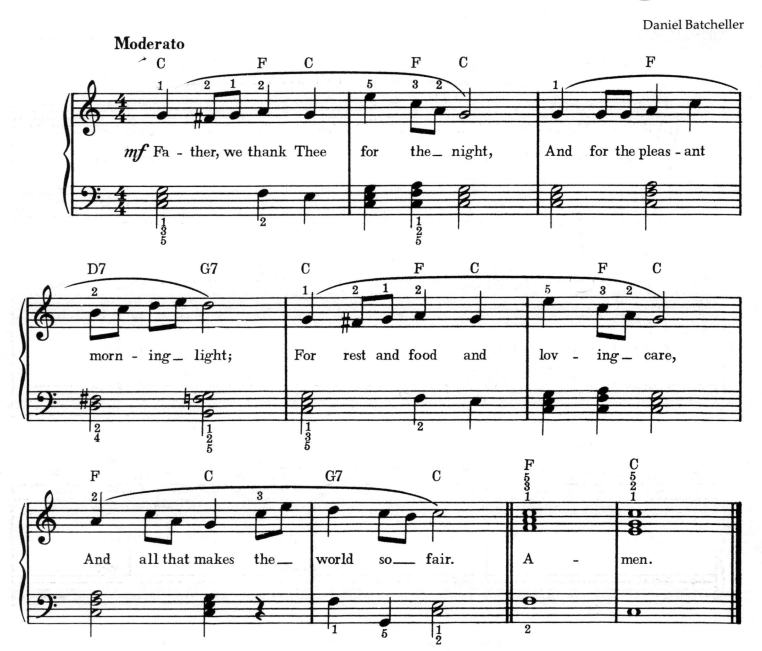

2. Help us to do the things we should,
   To be to others kind and good;
   In all we do, in work or play,
   To grow more loving every day.

Tell Me the Stories of Jesus

William H. Parker
(1845-1929)

Frederic A. Challinor
(1866-1952)

2. First let me hear how the children
   Stood round His knee,
   And I shall fancy His blessing
   Resting on me;
   Words full of kindness,
   Deeds full of grace,
   All in the love-light
   Of Jesus' face.

3. Into the city I'd follow
   The children's band,
   Waving a branch of the palm tree
   High in my hand;
   One of His heralds,
   Yes, I would sing
   Loudest hosannas,
   "Jesus is King!"

Jesus Loves the Little Children

George F. Root

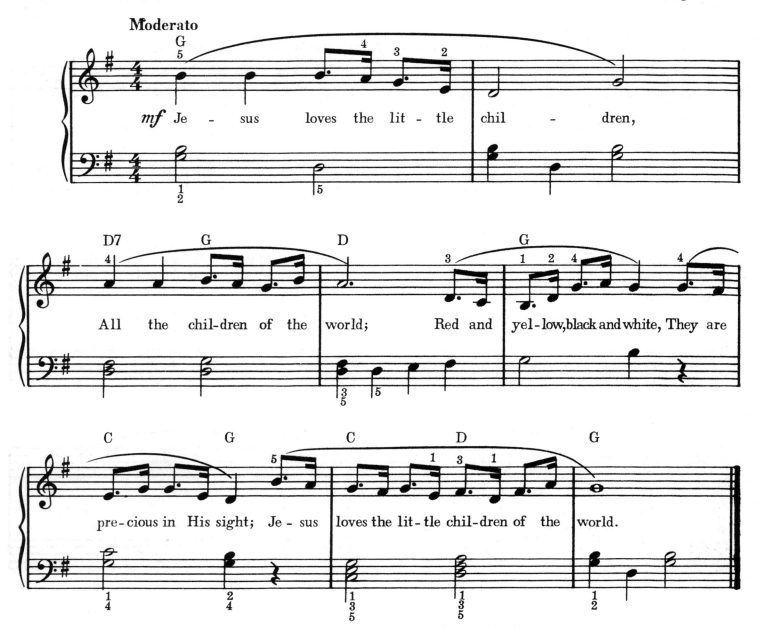

Praise the Lord

Praise Him, All Ye Little Children

Verses 2 and 3 by
James Bastien

Traditional Chil

Moderato
C F C
mf Praise Him, praise Him, all ye lit - tle chil - dren,
G C G7
God is love, God is love;
C F C
Praise Him, praise Him, all ye lit - tle chil - dren,
F G7 C F C
God is love, God is love. A - men.

2. Thank Him, thank Him, all ye little
children,
For the love He provides;
Thank Him, thank Him, all ye little
children,
For the love He provides.

3. Tell Him, tell Him, all ye little children,
Of your love for your God;
Tell Him, tell Him, all ye little children
Of your love for your God.

Father, Lead Me Day by Day

John P. Hopps

Georg C. Strattner

2. When in danger, make me brave,
   Make me know that Thou canst save;
   Keep me safe by Thy dear side;
   Let me in Thy love abide.

3. When I'm tempted to do wrong,
   Make me steadfast, wise, and strong;
   And when all alone I stand,
   Shield me with Thy mighty hand.

4. May I do the good I know,
   Serving gladly here below,
   Then at last go home to Thee,
   Evermore Thine own to be.

Sunday Morning

Dorothy Bastien

James Bastien

God's Watch

Dorothy Bastien

Jane Smisor Bastien

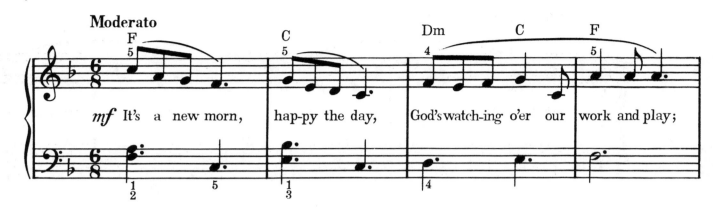

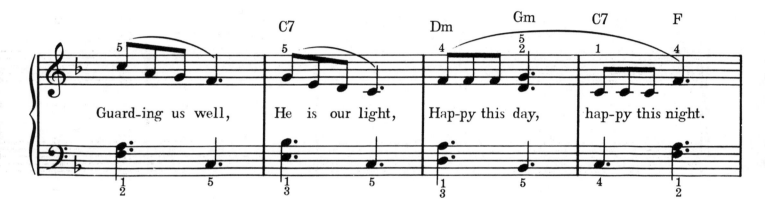

Faith

Dorothy Bastien

Jane Smisor Bastien

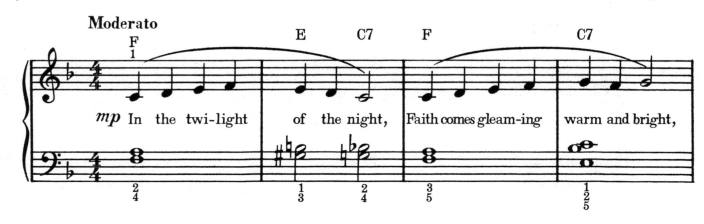

In the twi-light / of the night, / Faith comes gleam-ing / warm and bright,

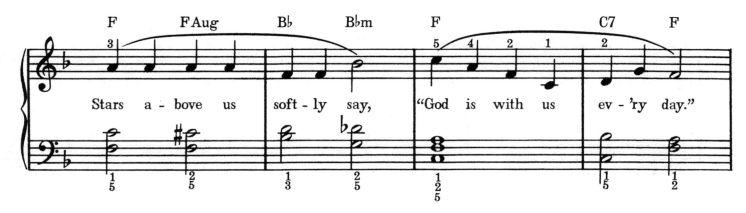

Stars a-bove us / soft-ly say, / "God is with us / ev-'ry day."

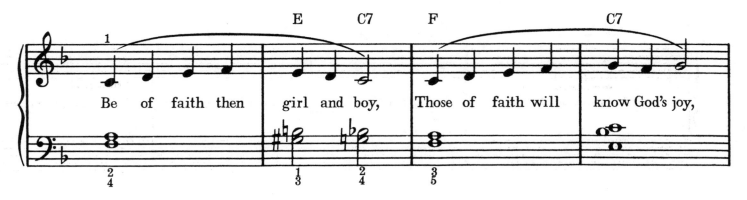

Be of faith then / girl and boy, / Those of faith will / know God's joy,

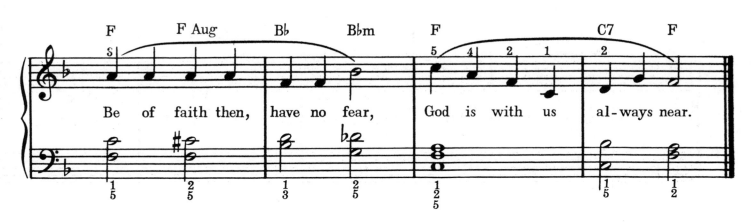

Be of faith then, / have no fear, / God is with us / al-ways near.

(WP41)

God's Touch

Dorothy Bastien

James Bastien

(WP41)

CONTEMPORARY HYMNS

Lord, You Are My Sunshine

James Bastien

James Bastien

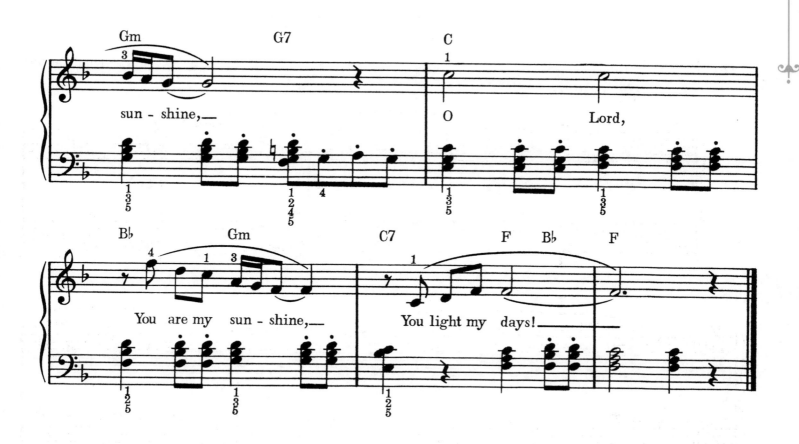

2. When things go wrong, and I feel kind
      of blue,
   I close my eyes, and I call on You;
   Comfort me, Lord, in my hour of need,
   I will follow where e're You will lead.
   Refrain:

3. When times are hard, and the goin'
      is rough,
   I close my eyes, and I call out Your name;
   Jesus, hear me now as I say,
   You are the light of every day.
   Refrain:

Count Your Blessings

James Bastien

James Bastien

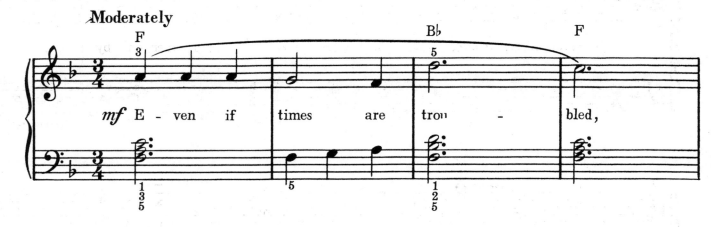

Moderately

mf E - ven if times are trou - bled,

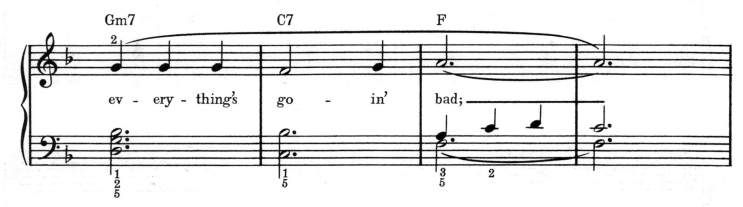

ev - ery - thing's go - in' bad;

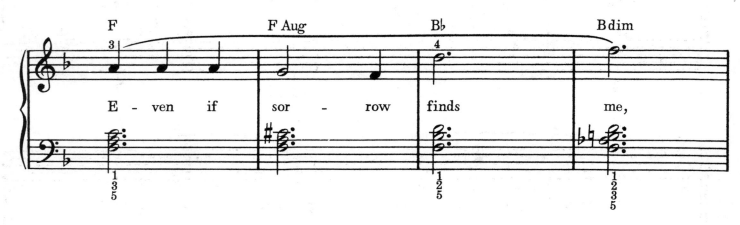

E - ven if sor - row finds me,

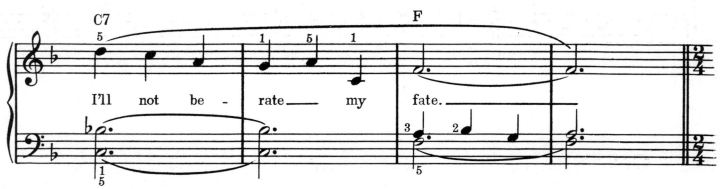

I'll not be - rate my fate.

2. Even if hardship finds me,
   Though I am down and out;
   Even if bad luck strikes me,
   I'll not complain my fate.
   Refrain:

3. Even if pain and anguish
   Keep me in torment;
   Even my load is heavy,
   I'll bear my burden in prayer.
   Refrain:

4. God has a plan and purpose
   For all us mortal men;
   Trust in God's love and mercy,
   Lay all our troubles there.
   Refrain: